www.Exploring Biology II: An Inquiry Approach

Frank A. Romano III | Benjamin G. Blair
Stacy Blair | William R. Bowen
Jacksonville State University

D1537281

CENGAGE
Learning™

Australia • Brazil • Japan • Korea • Mexico • Singapore • Spain • United Kingdom • United States

CENGAGE
Learning™

www.Exploring Biology II:
An Inquiry Approach

Frank A. Romano III | Benjamin G. Blair
Stacy Blair | William R. Bowen
Jacksonville State University

Executive Editor:
Michael Stranz

Custom Editor:
Katherine McNab

Custom Production Editor:
Jennifer Flinchpaugh

Project Coordinators:
Lisa Donahue, Peg Hagar

Senior Pre-Press Specialist:
Kathy Paxton

Production Supervisor-Labs:
Melanie Evans

Rights and Permissions Specialist:
Kalina Ingham Hintz

Marketing Specialist:
Sara Mercurio

Cover Image:
© Gerry Ellis / Digital Vision / Getty Images

For product information and technology assistance, contact us at
Cengage Learning Customer & Sales Support, 1-800-354-9706

For permission to use material from this text or product,
submit all requests online at **cengage.com/permissions**
Further permissions questions can be emailed to
permissionrequest@cengage.com

ISBN-13: 978-1-4240-7443-3

ISBN-10: 1-4240-7443-6

Cengage Learning
5191 Natorp Boulevard
Mason, OH 45040
USA

Cengage Learning is a leading provider of customized learning solutions with
office locations around the globe, including Singapore, the United Kingdom,
Australia, Mexico, Brazil, and Japan. Locate your local office at:
international.cengage.com/region

Cengage Learning products are represented in Canada by Nelson Education, Ltd.

Visit Signature Labs online at **signaturelabs.com**

Visit our corporate website at **cengage.com**

Printed in the United States of America

Contents

www.Investigative Project— Seed Plants

This lab is designed for use in distance learning programs.

*Prepared by Frank A. Romano III, Benjamin G. Blair, Stacy Blair
and William R. Bowen, Jacksonville State University*

OBJECTIVES

❏ Develop your powers of observation and inquiry.
❏ Translate and synthesize your observations into a coherent document or report.

You will be given some plant material in a dried, dormant state. Your goal will be to initiate growth in this plant, and to make as many observations of changes and/or events that occur within the time frame available. At the end, you will prepare a report from *your* observations.

COMMENTS

This lab is an exercise that you work on at home throughout the semester. You will have to make daily observations and measurements. All data collected should be recorded on your log-sheet and checked by your instructor weekly. Be sure to have all of your observations and measurements for Lab 21.

Safety Alert

✔ Some seeds are stained pink because they are coated with a fungicide. After handling, wash your hands carefully. Do not ingest any of the fungicide.

EXERCISE 13.1. THE LOG

Using the worksheet titled Assignment 13.1, *record* all procedures and observations *daily*. All observations must be *yours*. Your log *must* be certified weekly by your instructor and turned in along with your report at the end of this investigation.

Materials

- Peat disks (four) (part of your instructional kit)
- Plastic cups (five) (preferably clear)
- Bean seeds (eight) (part of your instructional kit)

- Transparent ruler (part of your instructional kit)
- Paper towel
- Water
- Thermometer (part of your instructional kit)

Procedure

1. Obtain eight seeds. Place four of these seeds in a plastic cup (Figure 13.1), and place the other four into peat pots in the other plastic cups.

2. Mark each plastic cup with your last name, date and time. Place wadded up paper towel inside one of the plastic cups. Place the seeds between the paper towels and cup sides so they are oriented in different directions, i.e., one pointing upwards, one pointing to each side, and one pointing downwards. Put water into the bottom of the cup, so that water moves up to the seeds via capillary action. Do not put too much water in the cup. If the seeds are overly moist they may become infected by a fungus and die. Keep enough moisture in the paper towels so the seeds are kept moist.

3. Place the four peat disks into each of the remaining plastic cups. Wet the disks so they swell up and are moist. They will expand to 4–5 cm (approximately 300%) in about 15 minutes (Figure 13.2). Do not let water remain in the cup once the peat disk has completely swollen, pour off excess water. With the pointed tip of a pencil, make a hole deep enough into the peat disk to place the seed so that it can be completely covered. Put the seed in the hole and gently push enough peat over the top to cover the hole. Place the cup in a well-lit window (if it is cold weather, place the cup in a warm well-lit area). Be sure to water the peat regularly, so that it doesn't dry out. Again, excessive moisture may cause the seed to become infected with a fungus and die, so keep the peat moist but not saturated.

4. Observe plant growth each day and measure the height of the plants every day. Make sure that you measure the length of each leaf, and that you are consistent with your measurements. Be as accurate as possible. Record this in your log.

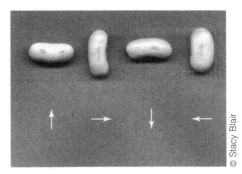

Figure 13.1

a) Lima bean; b) cup with paper towel; c) orientation of beans in cup

© Stacy Blair

Figure 13.2
Peat disks

- Record all observations/events in the log noting the *time elapsed* (in days) since the seeds were moistened.
- Once the seed has germinated, watch for any changes and/or structures that appear. Be sure to do this for all of the plants in all of the plastic cups, including the cup with paper towels and the cups with peat disks.
- Measure the length of any structures that emerge each day for seven weeks.

NOTE: You may find it useful to make a general drawing of the plants and smaller, more detailed drawings of any emerging structures.

---

5. REPEAT observations for seven weeks.

NOTE: Do not allow the peat disks to dry out.

---

6. Some questions to consider during the course of this project:

  1) What part of the plant (leaf, stem, root) was the first to emerge from the seed?

  2) Did the respective placement of the seeds in the plastic cup affect how each seed germinated, that is, which part emerged first, or how it grew? Did the parts growing out of the seed all grow in the same direction?

  3) Did any of the seeds have a different germination time? Did the parts of the germinating plant grow at the same rate?

  4) What was the rate of growth for the different seeds as they germinated?

  5) Did the seeds that were planted all grow at the same rate?

  6) What was the growth rate of each of your plants?

  These will need to be answered prior to the completion of Lab 21 and will be used in your report.

ADVANCE PREPARATIONS FOR FORTHCOMING LABS

LABORATORY 21—INVESTIGATIVE PROJECT: DATA COMPILATION AND ANALYSIS

The Report

You will need to write a report detailing your observations and interpretations of all structures and events that occur during your study from Lab 13. *Do not* include any information from a textbook or other source. This report is to be based solely on your observations. In Lab 21, you will be required to complete a report that analyzes and summarizes the data you and your classmates have collected.

This is strictly an exercise in helping to develop your powers of observation—a key aspect of the scientific process. What is required? Your report should be written in good, coherent English, that represents a synthesis of your observations.

Your report should include:

✔ An Introduction (brief statement of purpose)

✔ A Materials and Methods section

✔ An Observation (results) section (include your log)—be sure to tabulate all collected data

✔ A Discussion section (address questions, especially those you raise related to your observations)

✔ A Conclusion section (what you discovered)

All reports must be typed (word-processed), double-spaced and use a 12 point font so that they may be evaluated properly. The Introduction and Materials and Methods sections *should be* written before Lab 21.

Assignment 13.1-2

Seed Project Log-sheet

Date	Seed/Plant	Temperature (Celsius)	Plant Height	Root Growth*	Shoot Growth	Water Added (Y or N)
	1					
	2					
	3					
	4					
	5A					
	5B					
	5C					
	5D					
	1					
	2					
	3					
	4					
	5A					
	5B					
	5C					
	5D					
	1					
	2					
	3					
	4					
	5A					
	5B					
	5C					
	5D					

Date	Seed/Plant	Temperature (Celsius)	Plant Height	Root Growth*	Shoot Growth	Water Added (Y or N)
	1					
	2					
	3					
	4					
	5A					
	5B					
	5C					
	5D					
	1					
	2					
	3					
	4					
	5A					
	5B					
	5C					
	5D					
	1					
	2					
	3					
	4					
	5A					
	5B					
	5C					
	5D					
	1					
	2					
	3					
	4					
	5A					
	5B					
	5C					
	5D					

*Root growth should only be measured on the seeds with the paper towel. Remember to be extremely careful in measuring as not to injure the plant.

Assignment 13.1-3

Seed Project Log-sheet

Date	Seed/Plant	Temperature (Celsius)	Plant Height	Root Growth*	Shoot Growth	Water Added (Y or N)
	1					
	2					
	3					
	4					
	5A					
	5B					
	5C					
	5D					
	1					
	2					
	3					
	4					
	5A					
	5B					
	5C					
	5D					
	1					
	2					
	3					
	4					
	5A					
	5B					
	5C					
	5D					

Date	Seed/Plant	Temperature (Celsius)	Plant Height	Root Growth*	Shoot Growth	Water Added (Y or N)
	1					
	2					
	3					
	4					
	5A					
	5B					
	5C					
	5D					
	1					
	2					
	3					
	4					
	5A					
	5B					
	5C					
	5D					
	1					
	2					
	3					
	4					
	5A					
	5B					
	5C					
	5D					
	1					
	2					
	3					
	4					
	5A					
	5B					
	5C					
	5D					

*Root growth should only be measured on the seeds with the paper towel. Remember to be extremely careful in measuring as not to injure the plant.

Assignment 13.1-4

Seed Project Log-sheet

Date	Seed/Plant	Temperature (Celsius)	Plant Height	Root Growth*	Shoot Growth	Water Added (Y or N)
	1					
	2					
	3					
	4					
	5A					
	5B					
	5C					
	5D					
	1					
	2					
	3					
	4					
	5A					
	5B					
	5C					
	5D					
	1					
	2					
	3					
	4					
	5A					
	5B					
	5C					
	5D					

Date	Seed/Plant	Temperature (Celsius)	Plant Height	Root Growth*	Shoot Growth	Water Added (Y or N)
	1					
	2					
	3					
	4					
	5A					
	5B					
	5C					
	5D					
	1					
	2					
	3					
	4					
	5A					
	5B					
	5C					
	5D					
	1					
	2					
	3					
	4					
	5A					
	5B					
	5C					
	5D					
	1					
	2					
	3					
	4					
	5A					
	5B					
	5C					
	5D					

*Root growth should only be measured on the seeds with the paper towel. Remember to be extremely careful in measuring as not to injure the plant.

Assignment 13.1-5

Seed Project Log-sheet

Date	Seed/Plant	Temperature (Celsius)	Plant Height	Root Growth*	Shoot Growth	Water Added (Y or N)
	1					
	2					
	3					
	4					
	5A					
	5B					
	5C					
	5D					
	1					
	2					
	3					
	4					
	5A					
	5B					
	5C					
	5D					
	1					
	2					
	3					
	4					
	5A					
	5B					
	5C					
	5D					

Date	Seed/Plant	Temperature (Celsius)	Plant Height	Root Growth*	Shoot Growth	Water Added (Y or N)
	1					
	2					
	3					
	4					
	5A					
	5B					
	5C					
	5D					
	1					
	2					
	3					
	4					
	5A					
	5B					
	5C					
	5D					
	1					
	2					
	3					
	4					
	5A					
	5B					
	5C					
	5D					
	1					
	2					
	3					
	4					
	5A					
	5B					
	5C					
	5D					

*Root growth should only be measured on the seeds with the paper towel. Remember to be extremely careful in measuring as not to injure the plant.

Assignment 13.1-6

Seed Project Log-sheet

Date	Seed/Plant	Temperature (Celsius)	Plant Height	Root Growth*	Shoot Growth	Water Added (Y or N)
	1					
	2					
	3					
	4					
	5A					
	5B					
	5C					
	5D					
	1					
	2					
	3					
	4					
	5A					
	5B					
	5C					
	5D					
	1					
	2					
	3					
	4					
	5A					
	5B					
	5C					
	5D					

16 *www.Exploring Biology II: An Inquiry Approach*

Date	Seed/Plant	Temperature (Celsius)	Plant Height	Root Growth*	Shoot Growth	Water Added (Y or N)
	1					
	2					
	3					
	4					
	5A					
	5B					
	5C					
	5D					
	1					
	2					
	3					
	4					
	5A					
	5B					
	5C					
	5D					
	1					
	2					
	3					
	4					
	5A					
	5B					
	5C					
	5D					
	1					
	2					
	3					
	4					
	5A					
	5B					
	5C					
	5D					

*Root growth should only be measured on the seeds with the paper towel. Remember to be extremely careful in measuring as not to injure the plant.

Assignment 13.1-7

Seed Project Log-sheet

Date	Seed/Plant	Temperature (Celsius)	Plant Height	Root Growth*	Shoot Growth	Water Added (Y or N)
	1					
	2					
	3					
	4					
	5A					
	5B					
	5C					
	5D					
	1					
	2					
	3					
	4					
	5A					
	5B					
	5C					
	5D					
	1					
	2					
	3					
	4					
	5A					
	5B					
	5C					
	5D					

Date	Seed/Plant	Temperature (Celsius)	Plant Height	Root Growth*	Shoot Growth	Water Added (Y or N)
	1					
	2					
	3					
	4					
	5A					
	5B					
	5C					
	5D					
	1					
	2					
	3					
	4					
	5A					
	5B					
	5C					
	5D					
	1					
	2					
	3					
	4					
	5A					
	5B					
	5C					
	5D					
	1					
	2					
	3					
	4					
	5A					
	5B					
	5C					
	5D					

*Root growth should only be measured on the seeds with the paper towel. Remember to be extremely careful in measuring as not to injure the plant.

www.Responsiveness of an Organism

This lab is designed for use in distance learning programs.

*Prepared by Frank A. Romano III, Benjamin G. Blair, Stacy Blair
and William R. Bowen, Jacksonville State University*

COMMENTS

- This lab is an exercise in which you will be exploring certain life characteristics common to all organisms, whether single-celled or multicellular.

"Life" is defined by most dictionaries as the property that distinguishes the living from the dead, and they define "dead" as deprived of life. To most people, this is a meaningless definition. The problem is that one cannot hold or see life as it is not a separable, definable entity.

In this lab, you will discover some of the basic characteristics that we use to define life. From your readings, it should be common knowledge by now that to survive for more than a few minutes and into the next generation, an organism must be able to do the following:

- Gather nutrients
- Metabolize
- Respond to environmental stimuli/changes
- Escape predation
- Grow and develop
- Reproduce

Without these abilities the organism should not be able to survive, let alone live to be the progenitor of another generation. A quick review of physics tells us that any system must have a constant input of energy or the system will degrade and become more disorganized; think about what happens to an organism when it dies; its entropy (degree of disorder) increases. This is the 2nd Law of Thermodynamics. What does this mean to a living organism?

Without a constant input of nutrients, the organism will die (i.e., become more disorganized). What does an organism do with the nutrients it gathers? It uses them as the raw materials for its metabolism. From these, it produces all the energy and substances it needs to stay alive, grow, move, respond to stimuli, escape predation, and reproduce.

Biologists are trained to observe and provide logical reasons for every reaction of an organism. An organism must obtain water, nutrients, and mate, yet they must compete with all the other organisms in their specific environments, while at the same time avoiding things that can harm or inhibit their survival and ability to reproduce. This seems logical and simple but you will find that some organisms do things that are not immediately attributable to these criteria. Two rules that biologists have defined to explain how and why organisms respond to stimuli in their environment are Leibig's Law of the Minimum and Shelford's Law of Tolerances. These will be discussed separately below.

Leibig stated that the growth and reproduction of an organism is limited by the essential "element, nutrient or chemical" that is in limited concentration within the environment. An example of this would be to look at algae growing in a pond and then put fertilizer in the pond to observe the changes. The population of algae will "Bloom" and form mats of algae across the entire surface of the pond. Why? Because an essential element found in the fertilizer was in low concentrations in the pond and once an abundance of this element was available the algae grew out of control.

Shelford simply states that there are limits to the tolerance of each organism to physical and chemical stimuli in the environment. This includes things like temperature, pressure, acidity, oxygen, carbon dioxide and just about anything else you can think of that fits into these categories.

Energetics is the method of obtaining and using energy to efficiently improve the survival, growth and fecundity of an organism. This can easily be applied to many behaviors of biological organisms such as a cow eating grass. Some other examples that are of interest could include carnivorous plants (i.e. pitcher plant and venus fly trap). These carnivorous plants evolved in wetland bogs that have a low nitrogen concentration. Since Nitrogen is the element that limits growth in these environments these plants evolved two different methods of obtaining what they need.

Reproduction (fecundity) is one of the motivations that can affect the responsiveness of an organism in sometimes surprising ways. Why do some organisms put so much energy into the production of just one off-spring (humans, cows, elephants) and how does this compare to trees or parasites that produce large numbers of offspring? These responses are difficult to define and yet they can dramatically effect how an organism will respond to a threat. Many animals will abandon a nest under threat of a predator but many animal mothers are known to fiercely protect their young.

Symbiosis, defined as the interaction of two organisms in the environment, can dramatically affect organismal responses. Some of these relationships are known to be competitive when two organisms are competing for the same resource in the environment. A commensalistic relationship is a type of symbiotic relationship in which one organism benefits and the other is not effected, for example the small remora that eat scraps from a sharks meal. In fact, commensalism means to "eat at the same table." Predator/prey relationships should not need definition at this stage in your education but you should stop and think about the reasoning for heard behavior and why zebra's developed stripes. Competition between macroorganisms (those seen with the naked eye) or microorganisms are responsible for some of the most interesting behavioral modifications. Many of the chemicals produced by plants are in response to attack by insects or bacteria. Examples, include nicotine, aspirin, and many plant growth inhibitors. One example of how behavior can be unpredictable, until you understand the underlying reasons is, that when threatened by fire or insect damage, plants begin to secrete sugars from their root systems. This seems to counter the energentics rule. Most organisms only expend energy when it is absolutely necessary so why would they secrete the energy storage molecules (sugars) when they are in need of some major repairs? The answer is that they secrete these sugars to attract soil bacteria that produce antibiotics, in this way they can protect themselves from bacterial attack by transporting some of these antibiotics through the roots to the damaged areas of the plant.

EXERCISE 14.1. YEAST OBSERVATIONS

Today you will discover that simple organisms share life characteristics previously discussed. You will be working with three single-cell organisms; yeast (Figure 14.1), *Paramecia* (Figure 14.3), and *Euglena* (Figure 14.4).

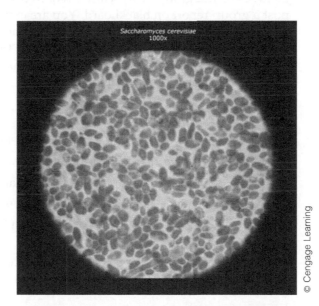

Figure 14.1
Saccharomyces cerevisiae

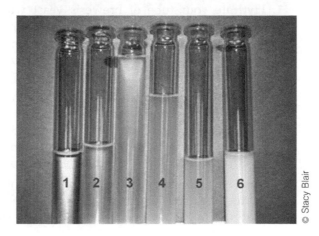

Figure 14.2
Turbidity scale

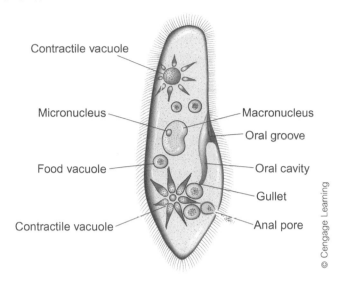

Figure 14.3
Paramecium

This is a normal baker or brewer's yeast and is not a pathogen. Each group will be assigned a set of experiments that can be easily replicated by each member of the group. You will be required to combine your results and post a group report on blackboard. You are expected to help determine the best method of working with the yeast for these experiments. Remember that scientists very rarely have an experiment that works perfectly the first time it is used. The yeast grow very rapidly and using the equipment you have available to you we would like to find ways of experimenting with their life cycles and preferences.

Materials

- Test Tubes (4) (part of your instructional kit)
- Yeast (part of your instructional kit)
- Transfer pipette (part of your instructional kit)
- Non-chlorinated water (you can make your own, see below!)
- Lemon juice, household chemicals, or salt or nutrients (depending on your group)
- Flour, sugar, oats, cereal, or cooked rice (depending on what you choose for your food source for the yeast)

Procedure

1. Hydrate your tube of brewer's yeast with 1 ml of non-chlorinated water and allow it to set (bloom) for five minutes. You will need to clip the end of the pipette with a pair of scissors. To obtain non-chlorinated water if using city or county water, boil 1/3 cup of tap water and let it cool to room temperature before using.

2. You may experiment with the nutrients that you grow your yeast with as a group. Examples: mix flour a set amount of flour with the non-chlorinated water and put 10 ml in each tube. Other food sources, sugar, oats, cereals, cooked rice etc. Please note that if you don't add a food source for your yeast they won't grow!

3. Take a transfer pipette and put one drop of the yeast mixture into each of the four tubes. One tube (tube 1) will be your control and should be placed at room temperature out of direct sun.

Group A – pH: In order to alter the pH of medium take lemon juice and put 10 drops in tube 2, 20 drops in tube 3 and 50 drops in tube 4.

Group B – Temperature: Place tube 2 in the refrigerator, tube 3 in a warm location or in a glass of warm water, and place tube 4 in boiling water for five minutes.

Group C – Chemicals: Place one, five and 10 drops of a household chemical or disinfectant into tubes 2, 3 and 4, respectively. You may choose any normal household items such as mouthwash, alcohol, and disinfectant soap (you may want to dilute if thick). Please communicate with the remainder of your group to coordinate your selections. You may all choose different items.

Group D – Salinity or osmotic pressure: Add 1/8 of a teaspoon of salt to tube 2, ¼ teaspoon to tube 3 and ½ teaspoon to tube 4. An alternative to salt would be to use sugar.

Group E – Nutrients: Dilute tube 2 by pulling out 5 ml of your nutrient solution and replacing it with non-chlorinated water, tube 3 by removing 7.5 ml and replacing it with water and for tube 4 remove all the medium and replace it with water. *Please note that you should do this prior to inoculating with the yeast.*

4. Observe the growth in each tube every 15 minutes for 2 hours and then check again after 24 hours.

5. Compare the turbidity of each of your tubes to the scale chart (Figure 14.2) and use this to report your results. You will report your findings on the worksheet titled Assignment 14.1.

After the 24-hour period you should carefully look at the settled yeast in the bottom of the tube. Make an observation on the amount of dead yeast in the control vs your experimental units.

EXERCISE 14.2. *PARAMECIUM* OBSERVATIONS

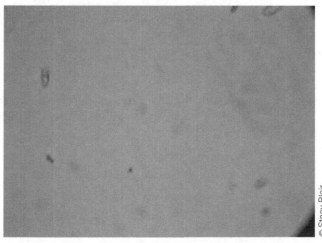

Video 14.1
Paramecium 1 (HP)

Procedure

1. View the video of the *Paramecia* after just being placed under the microscope. The video was taken using the high power objective (40X). How many times are these organisms magnified? _____

   How do they move?

   _____

   Please note that under normal conditions these organisms move so quickly that it might be difficult to determine how they are moving, therefore, Protoslo® has been added to the sample. This product will not harm the organism, but will make it much more difficult for them to move, thus, causing them to slow down.

   Do these organisms feed?_____

2. What would you expect to see after some stained yeast cells have been added to the sample?_____

   _____

   Would you expect to see these particles entering the *Paramecium*?

   _____

   They pull the food in by their ciliated groove, engulf the particles (called phagocytosis), and place them into food vacuoles. These act as "stomachs" for this organism. The food is digested and nutrients are removed, by diffusion, from the vacuole. Undigested wastes are excreted by emptying the food vacuole as it recombines with the plasma membrane of the organism.

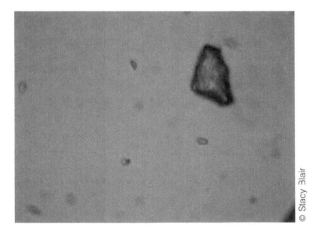

Video 14.2
Paramecium and salt 1 (HP)

© Stacy Blair

3. Finally, view the video of the *Paramecia* after a crystal of salt has been added to the sample. What happens when the *Paramecium* gets close to the salt?

   _____

   _____

   Why do you think they behave like this?

   _____

   _____

They can sense the dissolved salt as a noxious chemical that could harm them and they try to avoid it. The ability to sense the environment is another quality of life. So far, the *Paramecium* qualifies as a living organism.

EXERCISE 14.3. *EUGLENA* OBSERVATIONS

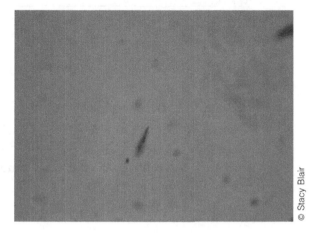

Video 14.3
Euglena 2 (HP)

© Stacy Blair

Procedure

1. View the video of the *Euglena* after just being placed under the microscope. The video was taken using the high power objective (40X).

   How do they move?_____

   Please note that under normal conditions these organisms move so quickly that it might be difficult to determine how they are moving, therefore, Protoslo® has been added to the sample. This product will

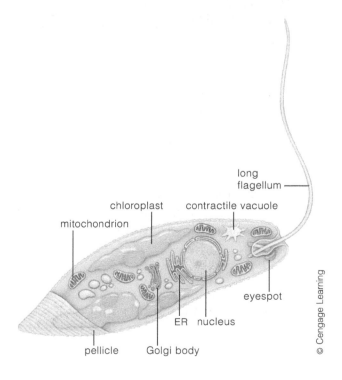

Figure 14.4
Euglena

© Cengage Learning

not harm the organisms but will make it much more difficult for them to move, thus, causing them to slow down.

Do these organisms feed?_____

2. Again, what would you expect to see after some stained yeast cells have been added to the sample?

_____

Would you expect to see the *Euglena* feeding on these particles? If not, why? _____

3. Finally, would you expect the *Euglena* to behave as the *Paramecium* did after a crystal of salt has been added to the sample?

_____

_____

Why do you think they behave like this?

_____

_____

They can sense the dissolved salt as a noxious chemical that could harm them and they try to avoid it. The ability to sense the environment is another quality of life. So far, the *Euglena* qualifies as a living organism.

EXERCISE 14.4. REACTIONS TO LIGHT

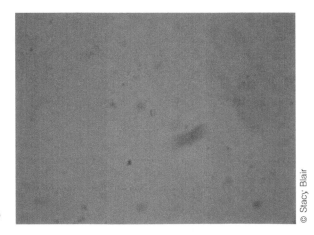

© Stacy Blair

www.blackboard.com

Video 14.4
Paramecium and Euglena (HP)

Procedure

1. View the video of the *Paramecium and Euglena* after just being placed under the microscope. The video was taken using the high power objective (40X). Do you see any interactions between these organisms?

_____

If so, describe what they are doing._____

Please note that under normal conditions these organisms move so quickly that it might be difficult to determine how they are moving, therefore, Protoslo® has been added to the sample. This product will not harm the organism, but will make it much more difficult for them to move, thus, causing them to slow down.

2. How would you expect the *Paramecia* and *Euglena* to behave after a black plastic disk with a slit cut down the center has been placed under the sample? This will allow a narrow beam of light through the sample.

_____

_____

Did the organisms segregate or remain together?_____

Why do you think they did this?_____

_____

Let me give you a hint – what color are *Euglena*?

_____

Do you think this has caused any behavioral differences? Why?

_____

_____

Again, the organisms are able to respond to the environment. Their response is known as a **taxism.** This is defined as a movement of freely mobile organisms or parts of organisms toward (positive taxis) or away from (negative taxis) a source of stimulation. In other words, this is a directional response to a stimulus. In this case the stimulus is light, so the organisms are **phototaxic.** *Paramecia* are negatively phototaxic, i.e., they move away from a source of light, while, *Euglena* are positively phototaxic in that they move toward a source of light. Both of these behaviors favor the survival of the organisms. *Paramecia* cannot be seen by predators as well in the dark; therefore, they survive longer. *Euglena*, being photosynthetic, need light to feed themselves, therefore, they seek out areas that are well lit.

www.The Practice of Taxonomy

This lab is designed for use in distance learning programs.

Prepared by Frank A. Romano III, Benjamin G. Blair, Stacy Blair and William R. Bowen, Jacksonville State University

OBJECTIVES

❏ Understand how one classifies organisms.
❏ Understand how taxonomic keys work.

Taxonomy is the science of classifying organisms. **Taxonomists** identify, name, describe, and classify organisms. When classifying organisms, taxonomists group them according to their similarities. The underlying goal of taxonomy and classification is to place related organisms (those sharing a common ancestor) together in the same group. A classification system, then, reflects the origins of organisms.

In a general sense, we are all taxonomists. Everyday we engage in taxonomic activities. We smell an unusual odor; we identify it. Our friends ask us about the food at a restaurant we frequent; we describe it for them. We name our children, pets, and art. Before we do the laundry, we classify our dirty clothes and group them according to certain similarities. Everyday we identify, describe, name, and classify.

Because much of what we do is taxonomic in essence, classification systems are not only all around us, but are central to the success of many businesses. A grocery store groups cold cereal, hot cereal, and other breakfast foods together in one place. Soups are separate from spices. Soft drinks are separate from alcoholic drinks. And yet, all beverages (other than fruit juices) are placed next to each other and away from groceries. The organization illustrated by grocery, and most other stores, is hierarchical. Classification systems are hierarchical in their structure.

A **hierarchical** organization includes different ranks with one or more positions at each rank. Consider the grocery store example. The highest rank may be type of food, which encompasses meats, vegetables, breads, and drinks. The rank of department occupies the next level down. Under vegetable types, departmental positions may include fresh vegetables, frozen vegetables, and canned vegetables. Each department may be subdivided into the rank of sections. Within the beverage department may be a carbonated drink section, a non-carbonated drink section, and a bottled water section. Within each section are shelves of regular soda, diet soda, and caffeine-free soda. Within each shelf are different brands. This hierarchical classification includes the ranks of type, department, section, shelf, and brand with one or more positions included in each rank.

Classification systems are methods of storing information so that the information can be easily retrieved. Consider that floor plans of stores are laid out according to the classification system in use. This is true of most stores and is obvious in department, grocery, hardware, and electronics stores. In the example of a hardware store, tool sections are next to each other with other departments containing nuts and bolts, plumbing, and flooring, nearby. Paints are not near tools and may even be on a separate floor. This structure both informs and enables customers in finding their desired items. If we enter a store looking for plumbing materials, we automatically turn away from paints, because we know plumbing materials will not be near paint. If, however, we see a shelf of sinks, we walk towards it knowing that all plumbing materials are grouped near each other. Like many stores, the classification systems constructed by taxonomists store information about organisms in such a way that all of us can easily access the information.

Classification systems used by taxonomists include the ranks of kingdom, phylum (division), class, order, family, genus, and species. Organisms are grouped together according to their overall similarities. Organisms can be similar in many ways. They may have similar external forms and internal structures. They may have similar metabolic processes. Their cells may be similar in shape and composition. They may synthesize similar compounds. Their DNA may be similar in its base sequence. Taxonomists consider all types of similarities (and differences) in classifying organisms. Each specimen depicted constitutes a species. Scientific names of species have two parts, the genus name and a specific name (epithet). For example, all dogs are placed in the genus *Canis*. Domesticated dogs have the scientific name, *Canis domestica*. Scientific names of species are always italicized or underlined.

EXERCISE 15.1. USING A DICHOTOMOUS KEY

Procedure

Using the following link: http://www.aces.edu/pubs/docs/A/ANR-0509/ANR-0509.pdf, wind your way thru the key in order to determine the scientific name for the illustrations depicted below (Figure 15.1a-c, Figures 15.2a-d, and Figures 15.3a-b). Be sure to record on the worksheet titled Assignment 15.1 each step of your logic and the reason that you selected the characteristic descriptions in determining the **scientific name** of the specimen. For example, in describing the eastern redcedar (*Juniperus virginiana*), first record "1. Leaves needle-like or scale-like; trees with cones." Then record "Conifers 1. Leaves scale-like, sometimes pointed on the end...cones occur only on female trees." Please, note that you may need to look up some of the definitions and terminology used in the key in order to make a proper identification.

© 2009 Jupiterimages Corporation

Figure 15.1
*a) Unknown tree A; b) unknown tree A, leaf upper surface;
c) unknown tree A, leaf lower surface*

Figure 15.2
a) Unknown tree B; b) unknown tree B, twig; c) unknown tree B, leaf upper surface; d) Unknown tree B, leaf lower surface

Figure 15.3
a) Unknown tree C;
b) unknown tree C, reproductive structure and leaf

www.Prokaryotic Diversity: The Microbes among Us

This lab is designed for use in distance learning programs.

Prepared by Frank A. Romano III, Benjamin G. Blair, Stacy Blair and William R. Bowen, Jacksonville State University

OBJECTIVES

❏ Gain an appreciation for the large number and diversity of bacteria in our environment.

COMMENTS

- Bacteria are all around us and most are not harmful; in fact, many are necessary for us to live.

NOTICE: You are instructed to fill out the questionnaire at the beginning of Lab 16 (this will be titled Assignment 16.1-1). This assignment should be complete prior to beginning the rest of the lab.

CLASSIFICATION

The Good

There are so many bacteria that if you were to remove all the plants, animals, and earth from this planet, there would still be a ghostly outline of everything. When most people think of bacteria, they only concentrate on the bad bacteria or those that cause you to get sick. This is natural; but in reality, less than one-tenth of one percent (1/10 of 1%) of all bacteria have any harmful effect on humans. As a matter of fact, most serve us in some manner. There is a brand new field of study, called **Probiotics**, which applies the use of good bacteria to treat or prevent disease. Think of it like this, there are only so many homes or niches within your gut. If they are filled with good bacteria, then there is no room for any bad bacteria to set up housekeeping. We employ bacteria to perform many tasks for us, including fermenting or preserving food, making cheese, breaking down harmful chemicals in the environment and most recently, making drugs through genetic engineering. The field of microbiology is broad and includes microorganisms other than bacteria. However, this exercise is only concerned with prokaryotes. The term prokaryote means "before the kernal" which roughly translated means before the nucleus. Bacteria are organisms that have no nucleus and are very small in comparison to one of our cells.

The Bad

Throughout history, man has been affected by our invisible neighbors, bacteria, whether we were aware of this or not. The primary way that we can trace this history is through disease. It was once thought that death and sickness were due to sin, or that they were punishments for wrongdoing. Now we know that many diseases can be directly attributed to the pathogenicity of bacteria. The term "pathogenicity" applied to the ability of certain sorts of bacteria to cause disease. It has been observed that individual strains in such a group might vary with respect to their "virulence". It is not uncommon for people to acquire pathogenic strains of bacteria through food that they eat, contact with other people, or through an open wound. We are also in an age where we read a great deal about antibiotic resistance in the popular press. What is antibiotic resistance? What can we do to help prevent this condition from causing us major problems? Since there are so many different disease-causing microorganisms, we will only give a few examples below.

Food-born diseases are not uncommon, and are usually associated with short-term food poisoning; results in vomiting, diarrhea, and headache, but can in extreme cases, result in *death*. One example of a food-born disease that occurs in the USA, is caused by the bacterium *Vibrio vulnificus*. It is usually associated with coastal regions of the Southeastern US, and involves the consumption of raw oysters. Conditions that facilitate mass infections in man include extremes in age (i.e. the very young or old), transplant patients, immunocompromised patients, and people with liver dysfunction. Even if you are in good health, it is not recommended that you consume raw or undercooked seafood/meats.

Diseases caused by person-to-person transfer are very common and, in places like hospitals, can be deadly! Hospital-acquired infections are known as **Nosocomial** infections and are transmitted person-to-person between patients of a hospital, either by casual contact or by the medial staff. Many hospitals are acutely aware of the problem, and keep a very close eye on the numbers of nosocomial infections that are attributed to any one group of workers. If the problem continues, every worker on a floor has to undergo testing, which includes nasal and anal swabs. The take-home message of this is to wash your hands frequently.

Most skin infections are acquired through some sort of trauma or damage to the skin. Bacteria such as *Streptococcus* spp. can travel through an open wound in your mouth and settle on scar tissue in your heart! This can be very bad and can result in a condition called **endocarditis.** It is very important to follow your dentist's instructions concerning medications, after any type of oral surgery (see antibiotic resistance below).

A question above asked "what is antibiotic resistance"? The answer to that question is not that some humans have become resistant to antibiotics, but that some bacteria have developed the ability to fight off the chemicals we depend on to fight infections. If this scares you a little, it should. We have overused antibiotics in the past. Prescribing an antibiotic when a patient comes in with a viral infection does absolutely nothing to cure the disease. Most common viral colds and flu last about a week. This is the reason many medical schools tell students that giving an antibiotic to a virally infected patient will allow them to recover in about 7 days, but without treatment they should get better in about a week! Not only have we overused antibiotics in the treatment of humans, but also in the treatment of food animals. Chickens, cows, and pigs regularly receive doses of antibiotics to fight infection. The constant use of antibiotics on the bacteria has allowed them to develop several methods of resistance to some of the most commonly used medications. Penicillin is rarely used anymore for the simple reason that it is no longer very effective. What can you do to help fight antibiotic resistant bacteria? You should always follow your doctor's instructions to the letter! If you are given antibiotics, take the correct doses at the prescribed times, and do not stop before you have finished the entire bottle. Just because you feel better, does not mean you are completely out of danger!

The Unusual

Bacteria are now known to live in some very unusual environments, including high acids, high salts, high pressures, high temperatures, and it has even been suggested that they exist on other planets! Watch the tabloid and legitimate press for some fantastic stories.

Bacteria are responsible for the disappearance of ships and planes in the Bermuda Triangle. The topography of the ocean floor in that region has submerged mountains, valleys, and cliffs. The overhangs collect detritus materials that settle from the surface (dead plankton and other organic material). Over the years, this has built up several thick layers that have allowed bacterial growth and methane gas production. Whenever there is a disturbance to the area (i.e. earthquake) these layers release large pockets of methane gas which change the specific gravity of the seawater and air directly above. If a ship or low flying plane is caught in this gas pocket, it sinks or immediately goes into a nosedive and then disappears without a trace.

Dollar for dollar it is much cheaper to grow biological weapons, than to work with conventional or nuclear weapons; if you think about it, all you need is a kitchen! This is not a new concept and has been used since at least the time of Alexander the Great. Before attacking a town, Alexander would put a dead animal into the stream leading into the town. If half of the men in town become sick, then attacking the town was much easier.

USE: FOOD PRESERVATION

Man learned very early that if you can preserve foods like milk, you can utilize it longer, resulting in less waste and less starvation! What happens when milk or meat remains at room temperature for several hours? They spoil because certain types of bacteria grow and produce foul tasting acids; however, if you pack meat in salt, it cures the meat and prevents spoilage. If we were to take a fish and place it on the counter top until the next class period, it would not smell very appetizing. Why does it work to dehydrate or pack meat in salt? The process of drying the meat removes water from the meat; water is an absolute requirement to supporting the life of a bacterium. If you dehydrate meat, then there is not enough moisture left to support bacterial growth. The salt also changes the osmotic pressure of the environment and prevents the bacteria from being able to obtain water.

Milk forms curds when it sours, or enough bacterial acids denature the proteins contained in the milk. This is a process very much like boiling an egg; the white portion turns solid after boiling. The same thing happens if you put acid into the white of an egg; the proteins denature and cause them to become solid. The milk curd is transformed into a solid mass by the production of microbial acids. If the solid curd is pressed to remove moisture, it will then slowly ripen into cheese. The type of microorganism that is present during the ripening stage determines the type of cheese. Fermentation is also utilized in making wine, beer, vinegar, and many chemicals, such as acetone.

Many other areas of food microbiology are concerned with preserving food through canning and sterilization methods. Many companies actively seek employees that have skills related to food microbiology.

EXERCISE 16.1. COLONY CHARACTERISTICS

Materials   • Illustrations of bacterial growth from various environments

Procedure   1. To obtain a clue regarding the identity of a bacterium, observe the colony characteristics on a solid medium. Using Figures 16.1 to 16.5, observe the growth of bacteria from various environments. Now closely examine the colonies. Describe the colony in as much detail as possible. (Refer to Figures 16.6 and 16.7 on the following pages.) Is it round? Is it flat? Does it have smooth or rough edges? Does it have a raised center? All of these characteristics serve as tools to help identify a bacterium, just like a police profile helps to identify a criminal. Write your description in the space provided on the worksheet titled Assignment 16.1–2.

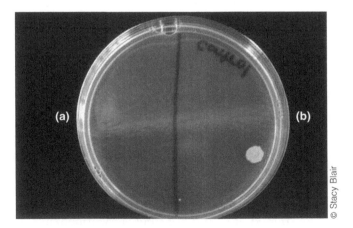

Figure 16.1
a) Control; b) control

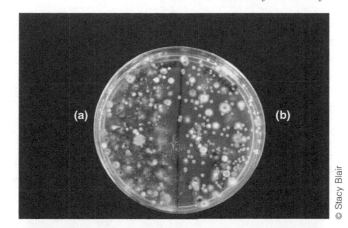

Figure 16.2
a) Leaf top; b) leaf bottom

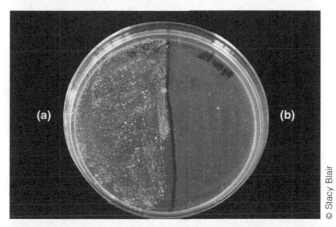

Figure 16.3
a) Skin; b) mouth

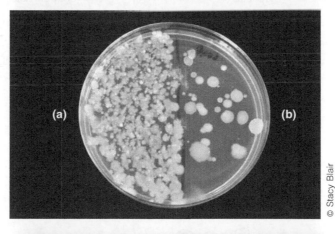

Figure 16.4
a) Root; b) leaf

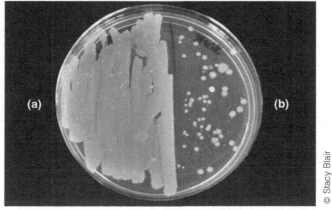

Figure 16.5
a) Water fountain; b) sink

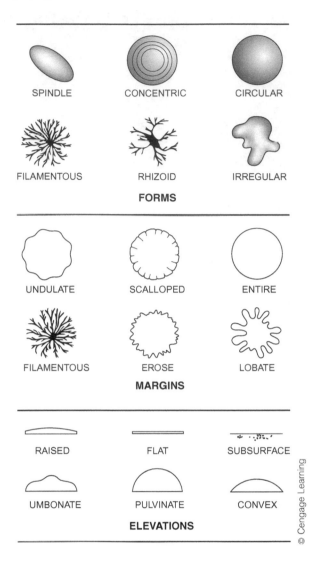

Figure 16.6
Bacterial colony forms

© Cengage Learning

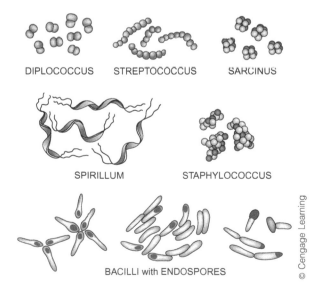

Figure 16.7
Bacterial forms

© Cengage Learning

Assignment 16.1-2: Colony Characteristics

Directions: Describe the colonies in as much detail as possible (refer to Figures 16.1 thru 16.7 from the laboratory procedure).

Plate 1 (Control)
Colony Characteristics:

_____

_____

_____

_____

Plate 2 (A) Leaf Top
Colony Characteristics:

_____

_____

_____

_____

Plate 2 (B) Leaf Bottom
Colony Characteristics:

_____

_____

_____

_____

Plate 3 (A) Skin
Colony Characteristics:

_____

_____

_____

_____

Plate 3 (B) Mouth
Colony Characteristics:

_____

_____

_____

_____

Plate 4 (A) Root
Colony Characteristics:

_____

_____

_____

_____

Plate 4 (B) Leaf
Colony Characteristics:

_____

_____

_____

_____

Plate 5 (A) Water Fountain
Colony Characteristics:

_____

_____

_____

_____

Plate 5 (B) Sink
Colony Characteristics:

_____

_____

_____

_____

www.Diversity of Life in Pond Water

This lab is designed for use in distance learning programs.

Prepared by Frank A. Romano III, Benjamin G. Blair, Stacy Blair and William R. Bowen, Jacksonville State University

OBJECTIVES

❏ Discover the diversity of life in an aquatic habitat.
❏ Gain the ability to use taxonomic keys.

Pond water unlike tap water is teeming with life. The organisms found in pond water may represent all six kingdoms of life (Archeobacteria, Cyanobacteria, Protista, Fungi, Plantae, and Animalia) and most are microscopic. Most people are quite surprised at the diversity of organisms living in the environment.

WHY IS IT IMPORTANT TO STUDY POND WATER?

It is often difficult for students to understand the importance of studying a specific subject. When you look through the microscope at a single drop of pond water you may be observing a cure for cancer or a new antibiotic. NASA is also very interested in working out a closed and self-sustaining environmental system for long term space flights that could use algae as a source of food and that works to recycle waste. What about finding an alternative to fossil fuels? There may be an answer in the sample you are observing. We simply need to ask the right questions.

The organisms found in your sample may be microscopic (smaller than 1 mm) or macroscopic (larger than 1 mm). Most organisms that you'll be able to see using the microscope will be eukaryotic and they will either be single-celled organisms or multicellular. How can you tell if an organism is composed of a single cell or multiple cells, especially if they are the same size?

For instance, you may find a large number of **protists** (Figure 17.1). These organisms belong to the kingdom Protista and are defined as single-celled eukaryotic organisms. They may be animal-like (commonly called

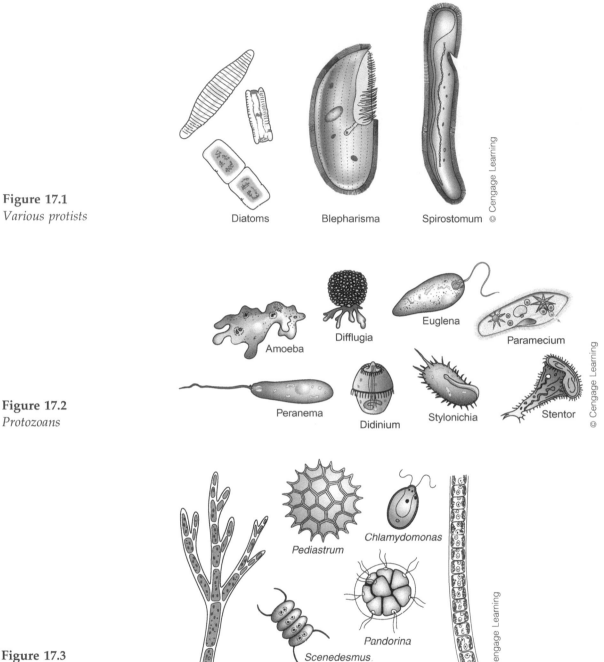

Figure 17.1
Various protists

Diatoms   Blepharisma   Spirostomum   © Cengage Learning

Figure 17.2
Protozoans

Amoeba   Difflugia   Euglena   Paramecium   Peranema   Didinium   Stylonichia   Stentor   © Cengage Learning

Figure 17.3
Various algae

Pediastrum   Chlamydomonas   Pandorina   Scenedesmus   Cladophora   Ulothrix   © Cengage Learning

Protozoa (Figure 17.2)) or they may be plant-like (commonly called **Algae** (Figure 17.3)) or they may be fungal-like. There may also be representatives of the kingdoms Plantae and Animalia. Plants, fungi, and animals are defined as multicellular eukaryotic organisms. How do they differ from each other? If you were given an organism to identify its kingdom, what clues would you use to separate them?

There are a large number of different kinds of organisms found within pond water and they can be found in several different habitats. Remember a habitat is defined as an organism's address. As you can imagine, there are many different habitats within a simple pond.

Types of Aquatic Environments

Neuston—living in the surface film

Epiphytic—living on plants

Epibiotic—living on animals

Planktonic—living in the water column

Benthic—living in or on the bottom

Each habitat can support organisms from any of the kingdoms. What types of organisms might you find in pond water? Below are descriptions of several interesting types of organisms that you may find.

TYPES OF ORGANISMS

Bacteria—All aquatic environments have a huge number of bacterial inhabitants. They exist in all areas of the environment and are key to the survival of everything within the system. Bacteria enter into relationships with all the organisms found within the aquatic habitat. Many bacteria in these environments are beneficial and aid in nitrogen fixation (basically fertilizer from the air), recycling sulfur and other natural elements, degrading dead organic matter and a very few are even pathogenic and cause the death of plants and animals. We are just beginning to understand that bacteria within aquatic habitats have a great deal of potential for our future. Many plants in these systems are prone to **biofouling**, a process by which algae, bacteria and fungi grow out of control over the surface of plants resulting in their "choking" and death. This is an epiphytic relationship where these organisms grow on the leaves of these plants. Biofouling occurs when these epiphytes grow out of control. If they cannot get enough sunlight because of the epiphytes (biofouling organisms) or cannot get enough oxygen or carbon dioxide they will die. Recently, scientists have found that some types of bacteria that grow epiphytically produce substances that prevent biofouling of other organisms. These substances have the potential to revolutionize businesses such as the shipping and paint industries. A large ocean traveling boat presents a very large surface area for these organisms to grow upon. Any of you that have lived on the coast and have had a boat know how quickly it can be fouled by these organisms and how difficult they are to scrape off. Marine scientists have come up with all sorts of recipes to prevent biofouling. If the substances can be isolated and produced in sufficient quantities to be added to paints for cruise ships and other maritime vessels, the result would be a great deal of saving in maintenance costs and great savings in operating costs. All those organisms growing on the boat's bottom not only increase its weight, but slows the boat due to its resistance in the water, increasing the amount of fuel used.

Millions of people across the world are suffering from many diseases. Many diseases are becoming resistant to the antibiotics that we currently use. Any new antibiotics identified could save hundreds of thousands of people from suffering or death. This laboratory will not focus on bacterial populations due to time and equipment concerns. It would require a great deal of time and specialized microscopes as well as other techniques to study the bacteria found in even one drop of pond water. However, when you find algae or a protozoan, you should be aware that they are interacting with the bacteria in the system. One interesting fact about bacteria in aquatic environments is that scientists have identified less than 1% of the bacteria found in these systems.

Biofilms are multiorganismal cooperatives of many different groups. You probably know of biofilms from walking barefoot in a stream.... Those slippery rocks are covered in biofilms. If you leave a wet sponge in a sink for too long then when you pick it up and squeeze it you find a large amount of slime. Biofilms are the major cause of death for cystic fibrosis patients and cause problems with implants (heart valve replacements or even metal pins inserted into bones). They are of major medical concern due to the fact that they are resistant to many of the antibiotics that we have come to rely on to save our lives. If you are a history major, consider the number and types of epidemics that have altered countless historical events. Migration of large numbers of people occurred to escape epidemics!

Biofilms can be found on the surface of anything you add to this environment. As a matter of fact, you can take a clean sterile glass rod and put into the pond water and in less than 0.7 seconds bacteria and algae will begin to colonize the surface. Biofilms are typically made up of bacteria, algae and fungi but are great places to find protozoans and animals that like to "graze" on these organisms. The slime trail left by many snails contains some complex sugars that stimulate the growth of specific biofilm inhabitants. The snails will then come back by and eat the slime trail picking up a snack of cultured organisms. Be on the lookout for biofilms on the surface of plant leaves or even on a grain of sand within your sample. If you choose an organism from a biofilm be sure to note that when you report your findings.

In addition to the bacteria, there are an incredible number of other organisms that may live in a pond. These organisms you will easily be able to view using a microscope and may represent all the other kingdoms of life. Some of the most obvious and interesting organisms that you may find include the **protists**, **algae, fungi** and **diatoms** (Figure 17.4).

Most protists are harmless to humans and go about their existence grazing on biofilms of bacteria and algae or eating each other. They make up a very important part of the food web and serve as a food source for insect larvae, small fish fry, tadpoles and others. Again, it is important to let you know why we study these organisms. The answer is that they impact our lives. Some are very sensitive to pollutants and when you kill

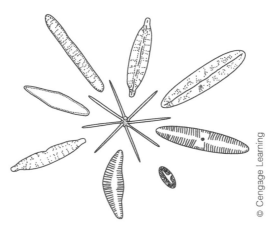

Figure 17.4
Diatoms

© Cengage Learning

them off, the animals that consume them loose a food source. Some prevent the overgrowth of algae in an aquatic environment. Still others are parasites and prey on animals and humans! One example of a parasitic protozoan that causes disease in humans here in the South is *Giardia lamblia* (aka-monkey face) which causes a disease commonly called "**Beaver Fever.**" It is associated with water contaminated with fecal material and is commonly found in the intestines of beavers (and muskrats), hence the name of the disease. This small pear shaped organism binds to the intestinal lining and secretes an enzyme that damages the intestinal cells. The disease symptoms include: severe abdominal pain, explosive diarrhea, lethargy (lack of energy), and in severe cases, jaundice due to infection of the gall bladder and liver. The Centers for Disease Control (CDC) view this as a reportable illness and it is considered by many to be a disease that can be used in terrorist activity. Many years ago there was one case of this disease being spread at an amusement park when a water fountain accidentally got hooked to a sewer line. There were cases of this disease popping up all over the country and the CDC had to track the source. The most common cause of the disease in this area is when people go swimming in ponds and streams where beavers and other animals have recently relieved themselves. It is difficult to find these organisms without practice since they are small and resemble a lot of the artifact in the sample. An artifact is generally organic material that is not recognizable such as degraded plant material. You can imagine all the 'cra....' artifacts that could be found in a fecal sample or even the sediment in your pond sample.

Not all of the organisms that you may find in your sample fit easily into one group or another. An example of a transitional organism includes the dinoflagellates (Figure 17.5). Some of these are responsible for the phenomenon known as "red tide" due to their photosynthetic activity yet they are classified as Protists. Dinoflagellates produce neurotoxins that can kill large organisms. They can be found in both fresh and saltwater and are of a major concern in streams located near large agricultural facilities that raise animals. The fecal material from the animals if allowed to enter the stream will cause a rapid growth in the dinoflagellate population and result in fish kills and sometimes even human effects. In marine environments, they can infect shellfish and the person who consumes it will get a disease called Paralytic Shellfish Poisoning within 30 minutes. The degree of symptoms is directly related to the dose and can cause numbness and paralysis to the point that death occurs. Death is caused by the diaphragm becoming paralyzed by the toxin, which causes the person to stop breathing. He or she wants to breath and are completely aware of what is happening, but can do nothing to save their own lives. History buffs should read reports of Captain Cook and Captain George Vancouver. Please, note that most algae in nature are non-toxic. They are simple plants that can be single-celled to

Figure 17.5
Dinoflagellates

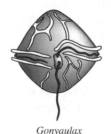

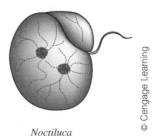

Gonyaulax　　　　　*Ceratium*　　　　　*Noctiluca*

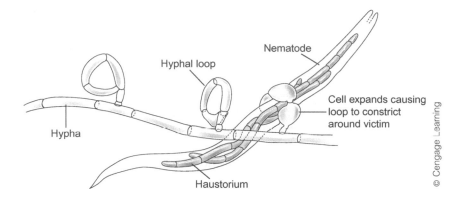

Figure 17.6
Nematode trapping fungus

long filamentous plant-like organisms. The largest are the kelps found growing off the coast of California, as well as brown algae, and are classified as protists.

Fungi are saprophytic (eat dead material) and can be found extensively throughout the pond but should be most concentrated in the mud on the bottom of the sample where you find the dead plant and animal material. One interesting fungus that can sometimes be found in the pond muck is the predatory fungus (Figure 17.6). Think about the term "predatory" which means to prey upon another. How can a fungus with no known method of locomotion become a predator? The answer is simple, they set traps. These fungi produce small rings of cells that act like a snare. When a small nematode (a worm-like creature) crawls through, the end the snare tightens causing the worm to be trapped. The fungus then begins to grow into the captured worm and literally eats it from the inside out.

The macroscopic organisms belonging to the plant and animal groups need no introduction. You should be able to easily describe and find some information on these interesting participants in the pond community.

EXERCISE 17.1. POND WATER DIVERSITY

Procedure

1. This exercise is to be conducted in groups. There are two portions to this exercise. For the first portion, the groups are as follows:

   Group A: Protozoans (excluding *Giardia lamblia*)
   Group B: Algae
   Group C: Freshwater Diatoms
   Group D: Freshwater Dinoflagellates
   Group E: Fungi (excluding the predatory fungus)

2. From the above group listings, choose an organism that interests you and then draw a representation of the organism on the worksheet titled Assignment 17.1-1. If possible, each group member should choose a different organism from their group.

3. Once you have chosen your organism, you should spend some time using additional resources (textbooks, encyclopedias, internet, etc.) to gather information about your organism.

4. For the second portion of the exercise, each group will have a video clip of an organism from a sample of pond water. The video was taken using (HP) magnification. Each member of the group will work together to identify their organism. The groups are as follows:

Video 17.1
Unknown A

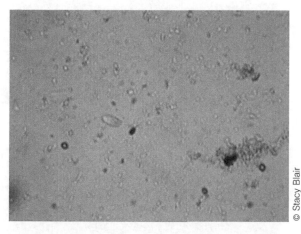

Video 17.2
Unknown B

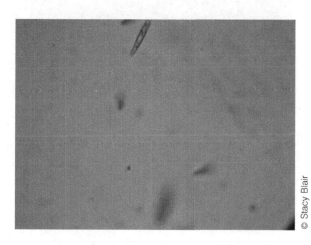

Video 17.3
Unknown C

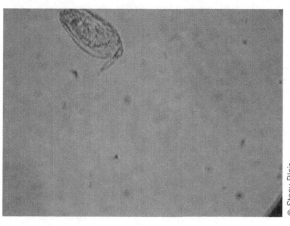

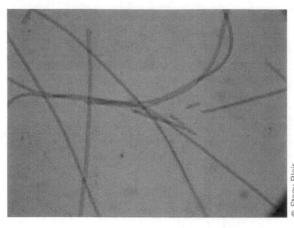

Video 17.4
Unknown D

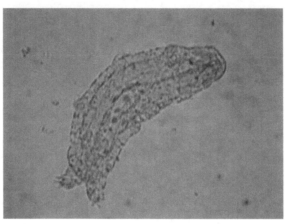

Video 17.5
Unknown E

5. Complete the worksheet titled Assignment 17.1-2 to help guide you in your investigation and post it to the class discussion board.

Assignment 17.1-1: Pond Water Diversity

Directions: Answer the following questions to help guide you in your investigation. This is to be conducted on the organism of your choice within your group.

1) What layer of the water column (upper 1/3, middle 1/3, lower 1/3) would your specimen most likely be found? Why?

2) Would it be found attached to a surface or floating/swimming in the water?

3) What is the size of your organism?

4) What is the shape of your organism?

5) In the space below draw or insert a picture of your organism.

6) Is your organism mobile?

7) What structures does your organism use for motility?

8) Does its shape help it survive? If so, how?

9) How does your organism feed itself?

10) What color is your organism?

11) Is your organism photosynthetic?

12) To what kingdom does your organism belong?

13) To what phylum (division) does your organism belong?

14) Did you find which family/genus/species it belongs?

15) What ecological role does this organism serve (herbivore, carnivore, detritivore)?

Name _____   Group _____   Lab Section _____

Assignment 17.1-2: Pond Water Diversity

Directions: Answer the following questions to help guide you in your investigation. This is to be conducted on the organism of your choice within your group.

1) What layer of the water column (upper 1/3, middle 1/3, lower 1/3) would your specimen most likely be found? Why?

2) Would it be found attached to a surface or floating/swimming in the water?
3) What is the size of your organism?
4) What is the shape of your organism?
5) In the space below draw or insert a picture of your organism.

6) Is your organism mobile?
7) What structures does your organism use for motility?
8) Does its shape help it survive? If so, how?

9) How does your organism feed itself?
10) What color is your organism?
11) Is your organism photosynthetic?
12) To what kingdom does your organism belong?
13) To what phylum (division) does your organism belong?
14) Did you find which family/genus/species it belongs?
15) What ecological role does this organism serve (herbivore, carnivore, detritivore)?

www.Exploring Vascular Plants I: Form and Function

This lab is designed for use in distance learning programs.

Prepared by Frank A. Romano III, Benjamin G. Blair, Stacy Blair and William R. Bowen, Jacksonville State University

OBJECTIVES

❑ Understand the phenomenon of transpiration and the role that stomata play.
❑ Witness that "Structure without function is a corpse; function without structure is a corpse" (Vogel, 1972).

COMMENTS

From lecture and/or textbook, you need to understand basic plant terminology. *Before* you begin this lab, *read* your text for background information on:

- Vascular plants: Ferns, conifers, flowering plants (monocots/dicots
- External features of the shoot (stem/leaves) and root systems
- Plant growth patterns (primary and secondary)
- Internal organization of stem and root (dermal/fundamental/vascular tissue systems)
- Related functional aspects: transport of water/nutrients; transpiration

INTRODUCTION

The **vascular plants,** originating some 600 million years ago, are now well-adapted through evolution to a terrestrial way of life. They include the **ferns** and the **seed plants,** specifically, the **conifers** and the **flowering plants—monocots and dicots.** The seed plants are unique due to their mode of reproduction (Lab 19).

In this lab, aspects of the non-reproductive structure and function of the vascular plants will be explored. Photosynthesis has already been considered; other functions include transpiration and growth patterns.

DO VASCULAR PLANTS LOSE WATER TO THE ATMOSPHERE?

Since vascular plants arrived on land some 600 million years, the phenomenon of **transpiration** (Figure 18.1) has been a part of their everyday lives. The loss of water through transpiration facilitates the uptake of water and nutrients from the soil and their subsequent transport and distribution throughout the vascular plant body.

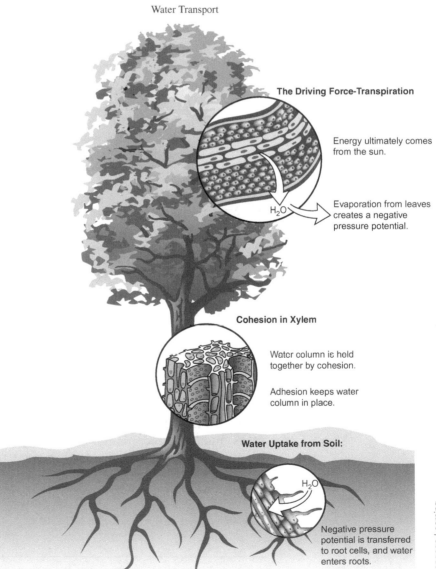

Figure 18.1
Water transpiration through plants

© Cengage Learning

EXERCISE 18.1. ENVIRONMENTAL IMPACT ON THE RATE OF TRANSPIRATION

You will participate in a group analysis of the impact that transpiration has on a plant. Each group will be assigned to measure the rate of transpiration under one of five different environmental conditions.

Materials

- Stalk of celery with the leafy shoot attached
- Test tube (from instructional kit)
- Fan (to generate wind)
- Lamp: preferably gooseneck (to generate heat)
- Oil spray (to coat leaf surfaces)
- Ruler (from instructional kit)
- Plastic wrap
- Razor blade (from instructional kit)

Procedure

1. Obtain a stalk of celery with the leafy shoot attached. Avoid wetting the leaves. Cut the basal end of the stem and place in 10 mls of water. Cover the top of the tube with plastic wrap so as to minimize evaporation of the water. Place the cut end of the stem through the plastic wrap and into the water.

2. Each group has been assigned one of the following experiments:

   Group A: Control. Room conditions. Skip to step 3.

   Group B: Heat. Place lamp close to leafy shoot. Turn it on to generate heat.

   Group C: Wind. Place fan close to shoot. Turn it on low speed.

   Group D: Heat and wind. Combination of heat and wind from groups C and D.

   Group E: Sealed leaf surface. Carefully coat the bottom of each leaf with an oil spray. The spray will effectively seal the leaf surface preventing the potential movement of water in and out of the leaf.

3. *Record*

   a) Water level in the pipette as TIME = 0

   b) The amount of water transpired in Table 18.1–18.5 on worksheet titled Assignment 18.1-1.

4. *Repeat* step 3 at 10 minute intervals for one hour. Calculate the average rate of transpiration in mls/hr. Record your data in Tables 18.1 through 18.5 on worksheet titled Assignment 18.1-1.

5. Prepare a **graph** of the rate of transpiration obtained by each of the 5 groups (control/experimental) on worksheet titled Assignment 18.1-2. *Label* each environment accordingly, i.e., control, heat, wind, heat/wind or sealed leaf surface.

Conclusions

From these experiments, it should be obvious that seed plants do take up and lose _____ to the environment. This phenomenon is **transpiration,** one of the major ways by which water returns to the atmosphere. While the water taken up from the soil is a liquid, what form does it take as it transpires back in the atmosphere? _____

What other gases are exchanged with the environment? _____

Which gas(es) diffuses in? _____

Which diffuses out? _____

One can argue that transpiration is a function detrimental to the well-being of a vascular plant. Are there any benefits? _____

_____

The question remains, *how* does the plant facilitate transpiration? The answer is partially evident in Group 5's data. The rest of the answer should become apparent in Exercise 18.5.

ASPECTS OF THE VASCULAR PLANT BODY

The seed-producing plants include the **ferns,** the **conifers** and the **flowering plants—the monocots and dicots.**

In the vascular plants, some of their external features are obvious, but others are not. The simplest vascular plant is that found in the fern. Its plant body usually is horizontal and underground. Vertical leaves called **fronds** emerge above ground; hence, the stem is called a **rhizome.**

EXERCISE 18.2. THE FERN PLANT BODY

Materials

- Illustrations:
  Fern with frond and exposed rhizome (Figure 18.2)
  Fern frond lower surface (Figure 18.3)

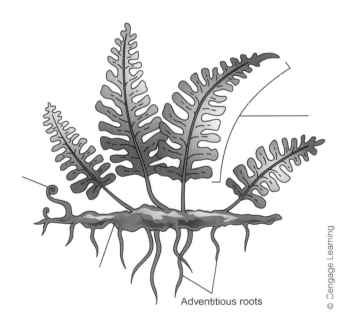

Figure 18.2
Fern with frond and rhizome

Adventitious roots

© Cengage Learning

© Stacy Blair

Figure 18.3
Fern frond, lower surface

Procedure   Examine the illustrations above and answer the questions on the work-sheet titled Assignment 18.2.

THE PRIMARY SEED PLANT BODY

In seed plants, a primary plant body emerges from the seed. It exhibits **primary growth,** a phenomenon that results in *an increase in the length of the entire plant body*—from root to shoot. Leaves occur *only* on the primary plant body.

EXERCISE 18.3. THE PRIMARY SEED PLANT BODY

Materials   • One bean plant from Lab 13

Procedure   1. Gently remove one bean plant from its container and place on a *damp* paper towel. Keep plant body *moist* at all times.
2. Observe the various portions of the plant (shoot, root) and answer the questions on the worksheet titled Assignment 18.3.

THE LEAF

The leaf occurs only on the primary plant body. Leaves exhibit consider-able variation, but those of each species are distinctive due to the particular set of leaf features they exhibit.

Root and Shoot Systems

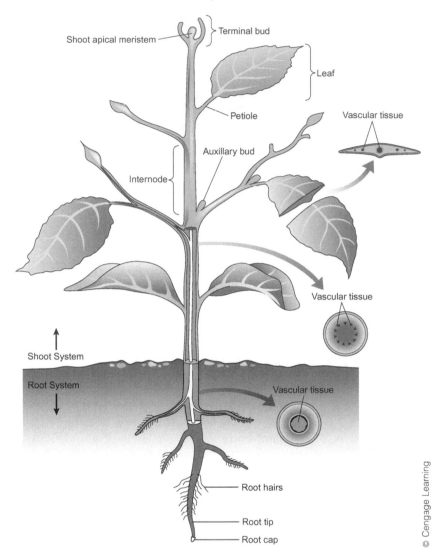

Figure 18.4
Plant body

© Cengage Learning

EXERCISE 18.4. THE DIFFERENT FACES OF A LEAF

Materials
- Examples of intact leaves (six), fresh or dried, all from different flowering plants (monocots and dicots)
- Plastic hand lens (part of your instructional kit)

Procedure

1. Carefully examine each leaf. Using the following diagrams of leaf types, arrangements, morphology, venation, and margins (Figures 18.5–18.8, respectively) determine which characteristic of these features is present. The characteristics presented are the most common ones.

Record your leaf observations in the table on worksheet titled Assignment 18.4.

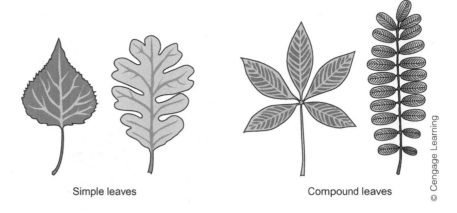

Figure 18.5
Simple and compound leaves

Simple leaves   Compound leaves

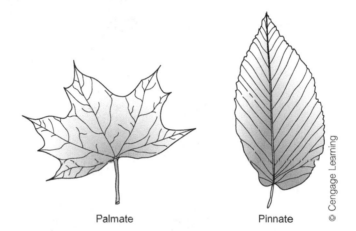

Figure 18.6
Palmate and pinnate leaves

Palmate   Pinnate

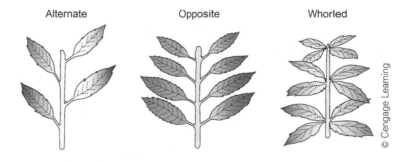

Figure 18.7
Leaf arrangements

Alternate   Opposite   Whorled

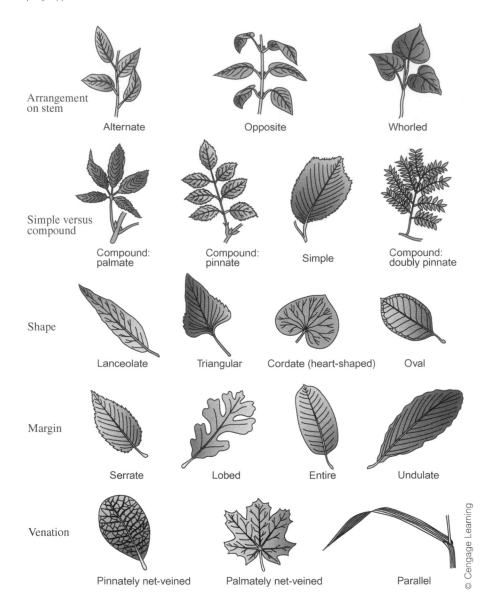

Figure 18.8
Leaf morphology

T H E   L E A F   S U R F A C E

Besides leaf hairs, either surface (upper, lower or both) may be porous or non-porous. Porous surfaces have "holes" or pores which can be seen only with a microscope. Each pore has the potential to open or close, depending on changes in the shape of the pair of specialized epidermal cells that comprise each structure. When open, the atmospheric environment is continuous with the leaf's internal space.

EXERCISE 18.5. THE POROUS LEAF SURFACE

Materials
- Illustration of leaf epidermis with guard cells (Figure 18.9(a)) and stomate (Figure 18.9(b))

Procedure
Complete the worksheet titled Assignment 18.5.

THE SECONDARY SEED PLANT BODY

Secondary plant growth results in *an increase in the circumference of the original primary plant body.* This expansion is superimposed on existing primary stem and root. Such growth occurs in both conifers and woody dicots.

EXERCISE 18.6. THE WOODY TWIG

Materials
- Illustration of the terminal bud cut longitudinally
- Fresh specimen: Intact woody twig, 4–6 inches in length, with terminal bud
- Plastic hand lens

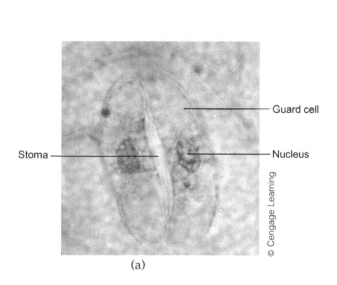

(a)

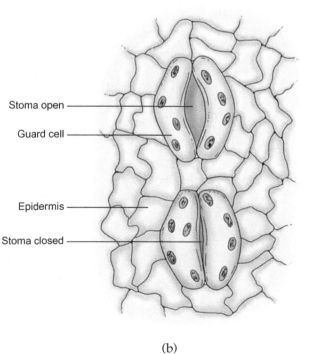

(b)

Figure 18.9
a) Leaf epidermis with guard cells (1000x); b) stomate

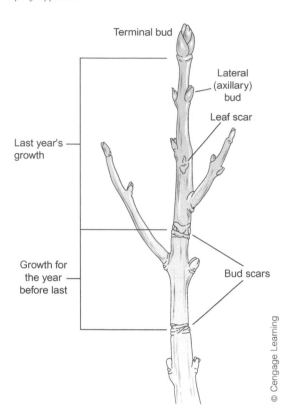

Terminal bud

Lateral
(axillary)
bud

Leaf scar

Last year's
growth

Growth for
the year
before last

Bud scars

© Cengage Learning

Figure 18.10
Woody twig anatomy

Procedure

1. Collect and examine an intact woody twig (please do not deface it) without leaves.

2. Study the illustration of the terminal bud cut longitudinally (Figure 18.11). You will see a 'herbaceous' primary shoot with leaves and stem inside the bud. Note how the leaves become smaller and smaller on the shoot near the tip or shoot apex. Compare with the bean plant.

3. Complete the worksheet titled Assignment 18.6.

© Stacy Blair

Figure 18.11
Terminal bud (l.s.)

INTERNAL ORGANIZATION OF THE VASCULAR PLANT BODY

The cells and tissues of all vascular plant bodies is organized into three tissue systems:

1) **Dermal,** consisting of a primary **epidermis** and a secondary corky **periderm** which is the outer part of a woody plant's **bark,** replacing the original epidermis

2) **Fundamental,** consisting of relatively simple cells that constitute the **cortex** or **pith** in the stem. The green fundamental tissue in a leaf is called the **mesophyll.**

3) **Vascular,** which contains the **xylem** responsible for transporting water and minerals up from the soil and throughout the plant body and the **phloem** which transports photosynthetic sugars produced in the leaf down to the stem and roots, and up to the growing tips of the plant.

This organization also reflects primary and secondary growth; hence, there are primary and secondary vascular plant bodies. The secondary plant body develops from within the existing primary plant body and becomes superimposed on it.

The internal organization of the vascular plant body is best studied in the stem.

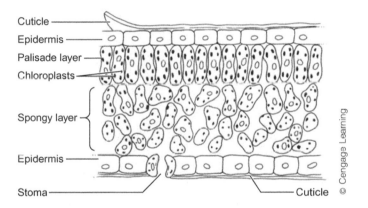

Figure 18.12
Leaf structure

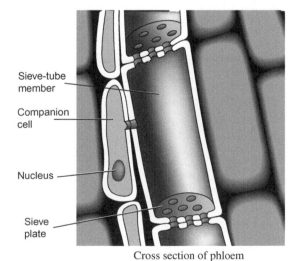

Cross section of phloem

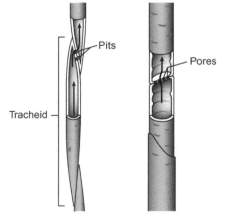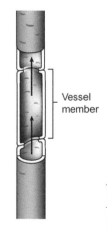

Vessels of xylem

Figure 18.13
Structure of phloem and xylem

Assignment 18.1-1: Rate of Transpiration

Directions: Record the amount of water transpired and calculate the average transpiration rate on the following tables.

Table 18.1 *Control group data*

Time (minutes)	Water Level Readings (mls)	Amount of Water Transpired
0		
10		
20		
30		
40		
50		
60		
	Average Transpiration Rate	=

Table 18.2 *Heat group data*

Time (minutes)	Water Level Readings (mls)	Amount of Water Transpired
0		
10		
20		
30		
40		
50		
60		
	Average Transpiration Rate	=

Table 18.3 *Wind group data*

Time (minutes)	Water Level Readings (mls)	Amount of Water Transpired
0		
10		
20		
30		
40		
50		
60		
	Average Transpiration Rate	=

Table 18.4 *Heat/wind group data*

Time (minutes)	Water Level Readings (mls)	Amount of Water Transpired
0		
10		
20		
30		
40		
50		
60		
	Average Transpiration Rate	=

Table 18.5 *Sealed leaf surface group data*

Time (minutes)	Water Level Readings (mls)	Amount of Water Transpired
0		
10		
20		
30		
40		
50		
60		
	Average Transpiration Rate	=

Assignment 18.1-2: Graph of Transpiration Rate

Directions: Graph the rate of transpiration obtained by your group.

Group:

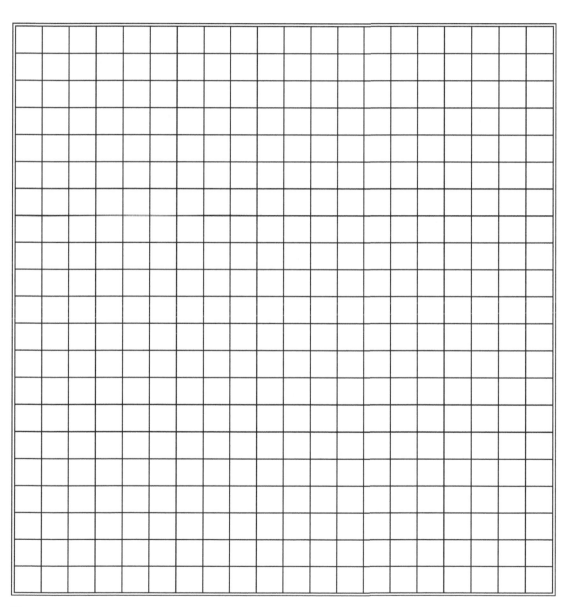

Figure 18.14
Transpiration measurements under varying conditions

Assignment 18.2: The Fern Plant Body

Directions: Using the illustrations in Exercise 18.2 and your textbook, fill in the blanks regarding the fern plant body.

1) The frond is the _____ of this vascular plant. Note the dissected or sub-divided nature. A well-developed rib occurs in the middle from bottom to top. What tissue does it represent?
_____

2) Note the small brownish areas (often round) on the lower surface. What do they represent? _____ Each area contains reproductive structures, the sporangia, which produce the fern's **spores** (see Lab 19 for their function).

3) The frond is attached to a horizontal part of the fern known as the rhizome. Note where the frond is (or was) attached to the rhizome. The presence of leaves on a rhizome means that the latter is actually
_____.

4) Do you find any roots attached? _____ They are not a substantive aspect of ferns; hence the ferns are limited in their distribution in the environment.

Assignment 18.3: The Primary Seed Plant Body

Directions: Observe the bean plant and answer the following questions.

1) Observe its organization. How would you describe its organization? That is, characterize the shoot and root. For example, which is white? _____ Green? _____ Above ground? _____ Below ground? _____ Why are the two parts so different? _____ _____ Is the "skin" continuous from the top of the plant body to the bottom?_____ What term scientifically describes the "skin"?

_____

2) Consider the shoot. Is the stem a rhizome? _____ The lowest leaves differ significantly from the ones above; they are a pair of shriveling bean-shaped leaves. These are the _____ leaves. The upper or true leaves are organized into a stalk called the _____ and a flat broad structure called the _____. Note the branching ribs on its surface; these are called _____ What kind venation does the bean leaf exhibit?_____ Is the surface of these leaves smooth? Or hairy? _____ What scientific term describes the point on the stem where one or more leaves are located? _____ The portion of the stem between each point of leaf attachment is called the _____. Where would you expect to find the shoot apical meristem? _____

What you should find is a tiny _____ bud. Now look at the junction between the stem and a leaf; is there a lateral _____ evident? Should it develop, what will it give rise to? _____

Is the stem smooth? Thorny? Or just plain fuzzy or hairy? _____

Do you find any external evidence of bark, brownish due to cork formation?_____

3) Consider the root. Where would you find the root apical meristem? _____ _____ Why is the root system white and not green?_____ _____

What is the main root that emerges from the seed called? It is a primary root but more frequently is called a _____.

Are secondary roots present? _____ These are more commonly called _____ roots.

Do you find leaves present on the root? _____ Nodes/internodes? _____ Examine the root tips. The pale yellowish covering over the end of the root is the _____.

Consider the plant's natural environment, what purpose would this "covering" serve?
_____

Where would you expect to find the root apical meristem? _____ If there are no lateral buds, how do these other roots originate? _____

Assuming the root has been kept moist, is there any "fuzz" on the roots just above the root tip? _____ If there is, each piece of fuzz is a **root hair.** What is its function? _____ The bean plant exhibits a primary plant body—monocot or dicot? _____.

Assignment 18.4: The Different Faces of a Leaf

Directions: Record your leaf observations in the tables below.

	Species #1	Species #2	Species #3
Type	_____	_____	_____
Arrangement	_____	_____	_____
Shape	_____	_____	_____
Venation	_____	_____	_____

	Species #4	Species #5	Species #6
Type	_____	_____	_____
Arrangement	_____	_____	_____
Shape	_____	_____	_____
Venation	_____	_____	_____

Assignment 18.5: The Porous Leaf Surface

Directions: Using Figure 18.9 from the laboratory procedure, answer the following questions.

1) Locate the bean-shaped pair of specialized cells. These are the _____ cells which constitute a stomate.

2) What are the tiny green bodies seen in each bean-shaped cell?

3) Compare these cells with the surrounding cells. How does the shape of normal epidermal cells differ from these bean-shaped ones?

4) Do the normal epidermal cells contain these green bodies?

5) What vascular plant function studies in Exercise 18.1 is facilitated by the presence of open stomata?

Assignment 18.6: The Woody Twig

Directions: Complete the following worksheet using the intact woody twig you collected.

1) Why is this twig woody?

2) Is it a woody dicot? Woody pine? How do you know?

3) Why are there no leaves?

4) What time interval existed between the terminal bud and the next terminal bud scar? Why?

5) The original epidermis has been replaced by the _____.

6) Why is there no secondary growth in the leaves?

7) Using the longitudinal section of the terminal bud, why would the shoot be called ''herbaceous'' or non-woody when in fact it is part of a woody twig?

8) On emergence in the spring, what part of this hidden young stem will elongate?

www.Exploring Vascular Plants II: Reproduction

This lab is designed for use in distance learning programs.

Prepared by Frank A. Romano III, Benjamin G. Blair, Stacy Blair and William R. Bowen, Jacksonville State University

OBJECTIVES

❑ Understand basic aspects of vascular plant reproduction—the role of the sporophyte and gametophyte.
❑ Understand the spore and pollen grains.
❑ Understand the nature of seed plant reproduction.
❑ Appreciate that cones and flowers represent modified shoots.
❑ Understand the role of pollination and fertilization in producing seeds.
❑ Understand the similarities and differences between mature pine cones and fruits.
❑ Appreciate the fruit and its variations.
❑ Appreciate the seed.

COMMENTS

Before beginning this lab, read your text for background information on:

• The life histories of the fern, the pine and the flowering plant
• What is meant by pollination and fertilzation
• An understanding of the pine cones and a flower
• The transformation of an ovule into a seed
• The transformation of an ovary into a fruit

INTRODUCTION

Reproduction in vascular plants in nature involves two generations of plants: a *spore-producing plant* or **sporophyte** that *alternates* with an inconspicuous and often hidden *gamete-producing plant* or **gametophyte** (Figure 19.1). The vascular plant we all recognize—be it a fern or conifer or a flowering plant—is always the spore-producing sporophyte. The **spores** it produces are minute, reproductive units whose formation involves meiosis. Spores form on modified "leaves" and, on release, are readily dispersed.

Each spore has the potential to develop directly into a new gamete-producing plant. Gametes in vascular plants form through mitosis and do not develop directly into a new plant. Instead, on release, gametes behave as **eggs** or **sperm.** Sperm are attracted to the egg, fusing together during fertilization to form a **zygote.** Only ferns require water for fertilization during reproduction; the seed plants do not. The zygote then develops into an embryo which is protected from the environment only in the seed plants.

Sexual reproduction (meiosis + fertilization) obviously requires both generations of alternating plants to complete the life cycle of vascular plants. Asexual reproduction (via mitosis) does occur in vascular plants, but today is more commonly achieved through cloning. You will now consider basic aspects of vascular plant reproduction.

THE FERNS

The fern is the only vascular plant in which both generations of alternating plants can be seen with the naked eye—but only if you know what to look for!

EXERCISE 19.1. EXPLORING REPRODUCTION IN THE FERN

Materials

- Illustrations:

  Fern sporophyll (Figure 19.2)

  Fern gametophyte and germinating sporophyte (Figure 19.3)

Procedure

1. Examine the illustration of the fern sporophyll. The sporophyll is a reproductive spore-producing fern frond. On its underside, note the masses of spore-producing structures. These differ from species to species and are structures that you have probably seen before. The individual spores however are much smaller and virtually invisible except with a microscope. The spores of individual species usually have distinct markings on the surface. Since they are not involved in fertilization, what do they develop into when they germinate?

2. Examine the illustration of a fern gametophyte and germinating sporophyte.

   Do you see any evidence of vascular tissue? _____
   Note the gamete-producing structures on the lower surface. Why the lower surface? Consider what environmental factor that is necessary for fertilization and the presence of motile (swimming) sperm?

   _____

   The gamete-producing plant will eventually die and the spore-producing plant will become independent. It repeats the fern's life cycle since the spore-producing phase does not develop directly from a spore.

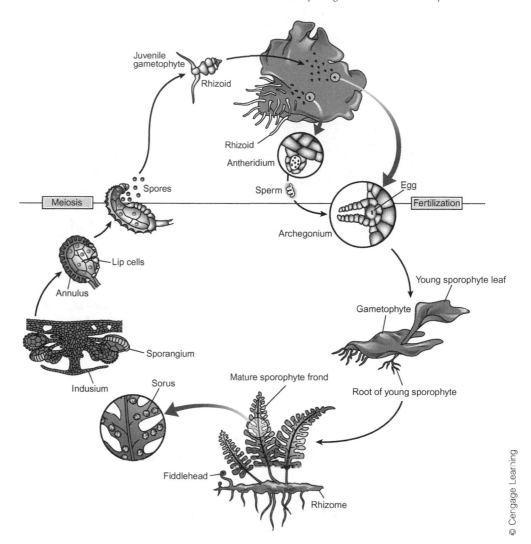

Figure 19.1
Fern life cycle

Figure 19.2
Fern sporophyll

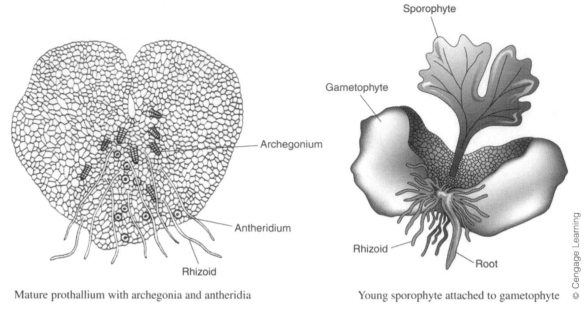

Mature prothallium with archegonia and antheridia

Young sporophyte attached to gametophyte

© Cengage Learning

Figure 19.3
Fern gametophyte and germinating sporophyte

REPRODUCTION IN THE SEED PLANT

Like the ferns, seed plants have alternating gametophyte and sporophyte generations. Unlike the fern, the gametophytic phase in seed plants is *highly reduced!* Why? Seed plants have evolutionarily circumvented the need for water during fertilization.

The overall reproductive structures in seed plants are highly modified "vegetative" shoots with most of the modified leaves or sporophylls comprising: a) the **cone** in conifers; and b) the **flower** in flowering plants. In both, male and female spores are produced. In pines, this involves male staminate and female ovulate cones.

Male spores are produced in structures known as **pollen sacs.** These spores transform into air-borne **pollen grains** which are dispersed via various means throughout the environment.

The process whereby pollen grains are transferred from the male part of these plants to the female part is **pollination.** Once pollination is complete, each pollen grain develops a **pollen tube** (a microscopic *male gametophyte!*) which grows down into the female part, delivering *non-motile* male gametes or "**sperm**" to a structure known as an ovule on the sporophyll. *No water is required to effect fertilization in seed plants.*

Meanwhile, the female spore has been retained within an **ovule** borne on a sporophyll of the parent seed plant. This spore develops into a microscopic *female gametophyte* containing one egg hidden within the ovule. As a sperm is delivered, it fuses with the egg (or fertilizes it). The fertilized egg is now the **zygote.** After fertilization, the zygote develops into a protected **embryo** while the ovule simultaneously transforms into a **seed.**

Seeds in pine mature within the female sporophylls and the female cone now comprises the **seed cone.** Whereas, in flowering plants, the seeds develop within the flower's **ovary.** As the ovules become seeds, the ovary transforms into a **fruit.** In contrast to the *open* pine seed cone, the fruit *encloses* mature seeds.

The seeds of both plants contain an "in-house" source of nutrients that sustain the embryo as it becomes a new sporophytic seed plant. Although evolutionarily reduced in size, the gametophytic generation in seed plants still represents an essential phase in the life of a seed plant.

UNDERSTANDING THE PINE CONE

The pine cone and flower are shoots modified for producing seeds. In both, the leaves of these modified shoots are spore-producing leaves known as **sporophylls.**

The sporophylls in pine are organized into two kinds of cones: a) the male cone (also called **staminate cone**) and b) the female cone (also called the **ovulate cone**). The male sporophylls of a staminate cone produce pollen sacs in male spores or pollen grains. The female sporophylls of an ovulate cone produce a female spore that is retained with an ovule on its inner surface.

EXERCISE 19.2. THE STAMINATE AND OVULATE PINE CONES

Materials

- Illustrations:

  Intact 1st year pine cones (male pollen cone and young female cone) (Figure 19.4)

  Male and female pine cone (l.s.) (Figure 19.5)

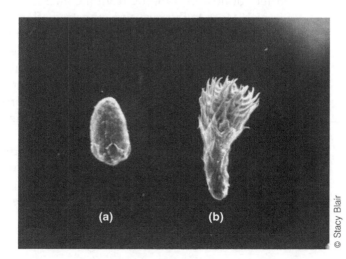

Figure 19.4

First year pine cones a) staminate and b) ovulate

(a)   (b)

© Stacy Blair

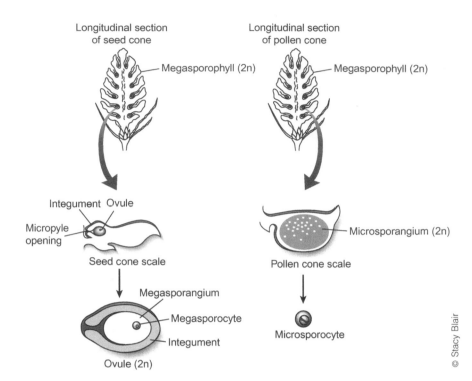

Figure 19.5
Staminate and ovulate pine cone (l.s.)

Procedure   Study the illustrations and answer the questions on the worksheet titled Assignment 19.1.

UNDERSTANDING THE FLOWER

Of relatively recent origin, the flowering plants are the most successful land plants due in large part to their mode of reproduction. The flower has co-evolved with a multitude of pollinators to create a seemingly infinite variety of flowers, ranging from the microscopic flowers of duckweed and Spanish Moss to the rare and monstrous flower of the Indonesian *Rafflesia* (approximately 1 meter wide). Did you know that Spanish Moss is a flowering plant, not a moss; it is related to pineapple and represents a most effective means of pollination. Flowering plants rely on other organisms to move the pollen from one flower to another rather than relying on the wind as pines do. In addition, seeds remain protected in the fruit, a closed container, until they mature. As in pine, remember the flower is a highly modified shoot.

Monocot and dicot flowers differ in the number of parts that comprise them. While flower parts occur in sets of **three** in monocots, the dicots have flower parts in sets of **four** or **five.** In contrast to the leaf-like non-reproductive parts, a flower's sporophylls are modified.

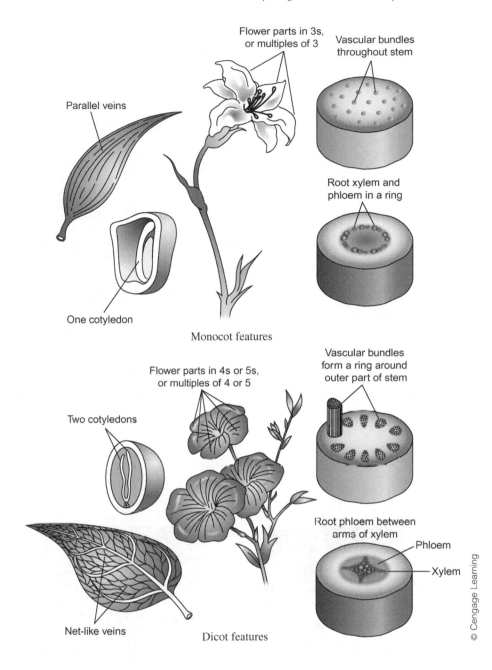

Figure 19.6
Comparison of monocots and dicots

EXERCISE 19.3. THE FLOWER

Materials
- Illustrations:
  Flower anatomy (Figure 19.7)
  Amaryllis a) whole flower and b) anthers and stigma (Figure 19.8)
  Ovary of apple (Figure 19.9)

Procedure

Review the illustrations of the flower anatomy, monocot, dicot, and ovary, respectively and answer the questions on the worksheet titled Assignment 19.2.

Flower Parts

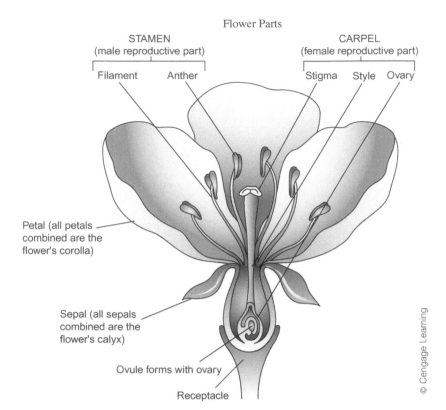

STAMEN
(male reproductive part)

CARPEL
(female reproductive part)

Filament   Anther

Stigma   Style   Ovary

Petal (all petals
combined are the
flower's corolla)

Sepal (all sepals
combined are the
flower's calyx)

Ovule forms with ovary

Receptacle

© Cengage Learning

Figure 19.7
Flower anatomy

Stigma

Style

Pollen

Anther

Filament

(a)

(b)

© Cengage Learning

Figure 19.8
Amaryllis a) whole flower; b) anthers and stigma

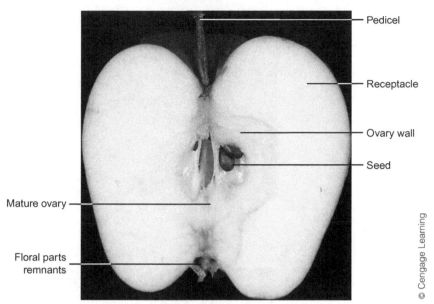

Figure 19.9
Ovary of apple

POLLEN

As you know from forensic science (i.e., CSI, etc.) and allergies, pollen grains have their own ID. While some flowers release wind-dispersed pollen, other flowers depend on a wide variety of pollinators, including many insects and some birds and bats. In fact, flowers and pollinators have frequently co-evolved with highly specific adaptations.

Each ovule produces a reduced female gametophyte bearing one egg. Pollination transfers pollen, either to the sporophylls of the young female pine cone or to the stigma of a flower's pistil. One might ask how one's species cone or flower recognizes pollen belonging to its species? It appears to be somewhat like an antigenic immune response.

Is the growth rate of a pollen tube towards the ovule the same in pines and flowering plants? No! In pines, it is exceedingly slow, the time interval between pollination and fertilization being 15 months. In contrast, it takes only a few weeks to a month in flowering plants.

In both instances, once a sperm interacts with an egg, fertilization is complete and it initiates more transformations.

EXERCISE 19.4. POLLEN AND POLLEN TUBE

Materials

- Illustrations:
  Pine pollen (Figure 19.10)
  Flowering (lily) pollen (Figure 19.11)
  Germinated pollen with pollen tube (Figure 19.12)

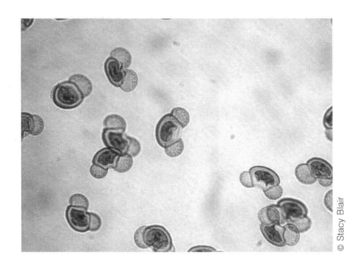

Figure 19.10
Pine pollen

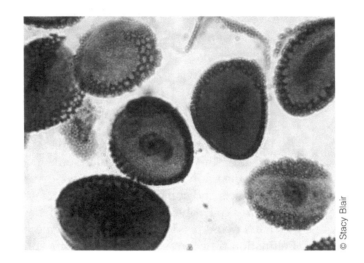

Figure 19.11
Flowering (lily) pollen

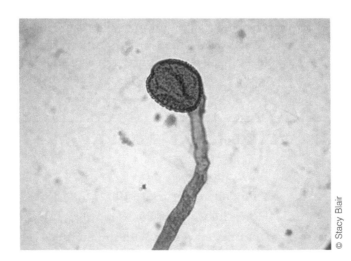

Figure 19.12
Germinated pollen with pollen tube

Procedure

1. Examine the illustrations (high power (HP) magnification) of the pine and flowering plant pollen below. Note the relative size and characteristic shape of each. What famous Disney character does the pine pollen resemble? _____

2. Observe the illustration of a germinated pollen grain and its emerging pollen tube. What do you think guides the pollen tube as it grows down through the style to female gametophyte's egg within an ovule? _____

_____

What does a pollen tube deliver to the egg? _____

Would a pollen tube fertilize more than one egg (and ovule)?

_____

Explain. _____

Is the growth rate of a pollen tube towards the ovule the same in pines and flowering plants. No! In pines, it is exceedlingly slow, the time interval between pollination and fertilization being 15 months. In contrast, it takes only a few weeks to a month in flowering plants.

In both instances, once a sperm interacts with an egg, fertilization is completed. And fertilization initiates more transformations.

THE PINE SEED CONE

The female pine cone matures as "fertilized" ovules begin to transform into seeds. The result is a **seed cone.**

EXERCISE 19.5. THE PINE SEED CONE

Materials

• Illustrations:

First-year ovulate cone, second-year ovulate cone (sectioned longitudinally) and winged seed (Figure 19.13)

Second-year female pine cone (sectioned longitudinally) (Figure 19.14)

Procedure

Study the 2nd year female cone illustrations. Measure the length and width in mm: _____ L × _____ W. Estimate percent change in size from that of the 1st year ovulate cone: _____ %

Note the distribution of sporophylls attached to the stem in this cone in sectional view. Does the cone resemble a modified shoot?

_____

Figure 19.13
First-year pine ovulate cone, second-year ovulate cone, and winged seed

Figure 19.14
Second-year ovulate cone

THE FRUIT

In contrast, as seeds develop in the flower, the ovary transforms into the **fruit** enclosing the seeds. The diversity of fruits is considerable.

    I. Simple fruits, derived from one carpel or several fused carpels

        A. *Dry fruit,* where the fruit wall is papery or leathery at maturity

            1. Dehiscent, having seams that open at maturity

                a. Follicle, derived from one carpel, splitting open along seams
                    Example: milkweed

                b. Legume, derived from carpel, splitting open along two seams
                    Example: peanut

                c. Capsule, derived from more than one carpel, splits along several seams
                    Example: cotton

2. <u>Indehiscent</u>, fruit does not open along seams

    a. Grain (caryopsis), seed coat fused with ovary wall
    Example: corn

    b. Nut, ovary wall is woody
    Example: pecan

    c. Achene, seed coat not fused with ovary wall
    Example: sunflower

    d. Samara, ovary wall forms a wing-like structure
    Example: maple

B. Fleshy fruit, where ovary wall is fleshy at maturity

1. <u>Superior ovary</u>, ovary is free and above receptable

    a. Berry, ovary wall is fleshy
    Examples: tomato, grape

Fruits

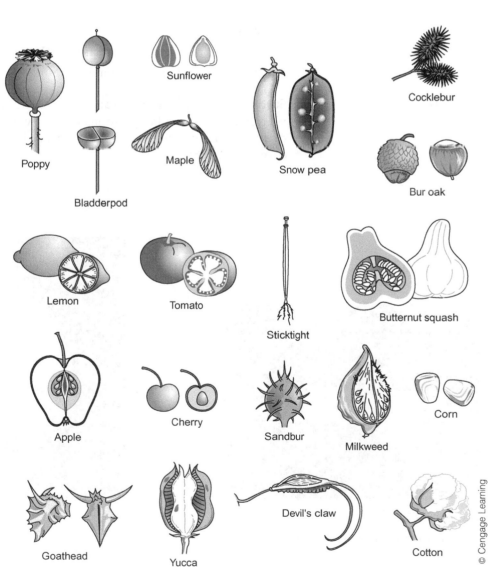

Figure 19.15
Various fruits

> **b. Drupe,** same as berry, with woody interior
> *Examples*: peach, plum

2. <u>Inferior ovary,</u> which is more or less fused with sepals

> **a. False berry,** ovary wall and floral tube (sepals, petals) are fleshy
> *Examples*: cucumber, squash, banana

> **b. Pome,** same as false berry, with leathery interior
> *Examples*: apple, pear

II. **Aggregate fruit,** derived from several carpels, ovaries fuse into one
Example: strawberry

III. **Multiple fruit,** derived from a cluster of flowers
Example: pineapple

EXERCISE 19.6. FRUIT

Materials

- Illustrations:
  Cucumber, whole and cross-sectioned (Figure 19.16)
  Apple, whole and cross-sectioned (Figure 19.17)

Procedure

1. Study the illustrations of the apple and cucumber (intact and sectional views) and answer the questions on the worksheet titled 19.1. As the ovary of fleshy fruits grows and ripens, it also differentiates into a complex structure.

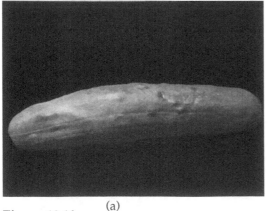

(a)

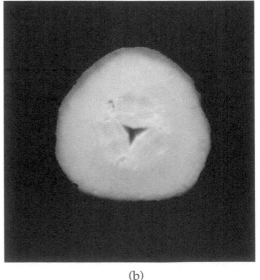

(b)

Figure 19.16

Cucumber a) whole; b) cross-section

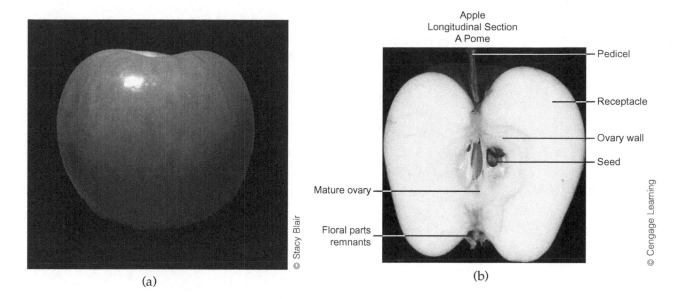

Figure 19.17
Apple a) whole; b) cross-section

THE SEED

In seed plants, the fertilized ovule becomes a **seed.** All seeds contain:

a) An **embryo** with one or more cotyledons (seed leaves)

b) **Endosperm**

c) A **seed coat** is the outer part of the original ovule. The seed coat now serves to protect the seed until suitable environmental conditions are available for germination.

In addition, most exhibit:

d) a **hilum,** the scar where the ovule/seed was previously attached to the ovary

e) a **micropyle,** the small opening through which the pollen tube grew

EXERCISE 19.7. THE SEED

Materials

- Illustrations:

   Pine seed (Figure 19.18)

   Dicot seed (Figure 19.19)

   Seedlings of bean and corn (Figure 19.20)

   Corn kernel (Figure 19.21)

Procedure

Observe the pine, bean, and corn seed illustrations, respectively and answer the questions on the worksheet titled Assignment 19.2.

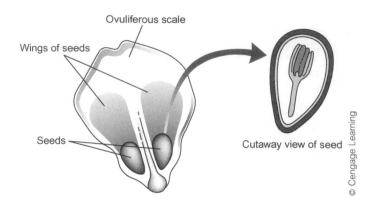

Figure 19.18
Pine seed

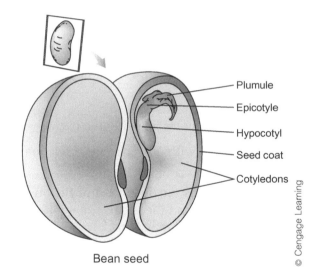

Figure 19.19
Dicot seed

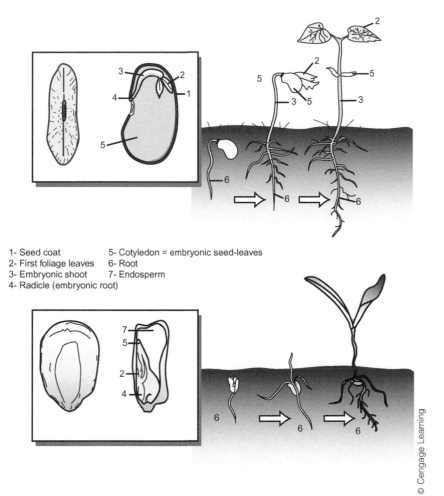

1- Seed coat   5- Cotyledon = embryonic seed-leaves
2- First foliage leaves   6- Root
3- Embryonic shoot   7- Endosperm
4- Radicle (embryonic root)

© Cengage Learning

Figure 19.20
Seedlings of bean and corn

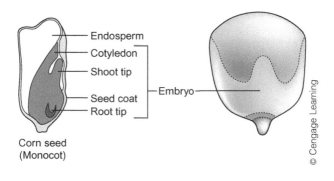

Endosperm
Cotyledon
Shoot tip
Seed coat
Root tip

Embryo

Corn seed
(Monocot)

© Cengage Learning

Figure 19.21
Corn kernel

Assignment 19.1: Fruit

Directions: Using the illustrations from the procedure and the information from your textbook or internet, answer the following questions regarding the fruit.

1) Examine the cucumber fruit. How many structural layers are present? _____
Study the cucumber in cross-section. How many units of seeds in cavities are apparent? _____
From your observations, can you determine how many carpels (sporophyll, each with a cluster of seeds) are present in this fruit (and therefore in the original ovary)?

_____

Label the illustration of the cucumber, **carpels, seeds.**

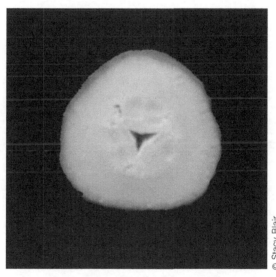

© Stacy Blair

Cucumber (Cross-section)

2) Now examine the apple in cross-section. What does the apple "core" represent (i.e., from the original ovary)?_____
_____ The number of carpels (i.e., chambers) in this fruit is? _____ Since the flesh of this fruit is not part of the ovary, can you guess where it came from? _____

Assignment 19.2: The Seed

Directions: Using the illustrations from the procedure and the information from your textbook or internet, answer the following questions regarding the seed.

1) Observe the pine seed illustration; it has been sectioned lengthwise. Identify the three basic parts of this seed. What color is the embryo? _____
    _____ What is the embryo's function? _____
    _____

    Does the number of cotyledons appear to be greater than two? _____.

2) Observe the bean seed illustrations. Examine the outer surface. Locate the hilum and micropyle. What is the function of each?_____
    _____

    _____

    Is the bean a monocot? Or dicot? The most obvious structure is the cotyledon. How many cotyledons are there? _____   This makes the bean a _____ plant.

3) What is meant by **double fertilization**? _____
    _____

    It occurs in which kind of seed plants? _____

www.Animal Diversity

This lab is designed for use in distance learning programs.

Prepared by Frank A. Romano III, Benjamin G. Blair, Stacy Blair and William R. Bowen, Jacksonville State University

OBJECTIVES

❑ Understand that animals exist in great diversity.
❑ Become aware that similar body forms can be found across all major phyla.

As you look around your environment, you may notice the tremendous diversity of living organisms. There are many different kinds of plants, grasses, shrubs, and trees. You may also notice lots of animals, insects, birds, and mammals. What you don't see are all the animals hidden in the plants, soil, and water. These may be animals large enough to see, such as earthworms, or microscopic, such as tardigrades. The current estimate of the number of different animal species on this planet ranges from 3–30 million. All of these animals are currently grouped into 35–40 phyla. Of all these phyla, only nine are considered to be major phyla. A major phylum contains animals that have an ecological and/or economic impact. The major phyla are as follows:

Porifera (sponges)   Cnidaria (jellyfish-corals)
Platyhelminthes (flatworms)   Nematoda (round worms)
Annelida (segmented worms)   Arthropoda (insects-crustaceans)
Mollusca (snails-squid)   Echinodermata (sea stars-sea urchins)
Chordata (tunicates-vertebrates)

Each phylum has its own special characteristics that allow taxonomists to categorize individual animals into each of the various phyla. A good example of this is our own phylum, phylum Chordata. Chordates all share four essential features that form sometime during their lives. These are a notochord, a dorsal hollow nerve cord, pharyngeal gill slits, and a post-anal tail. All chordates even humans, share these characteristics and any animal that is discovered with these characteristics is considered to be a chordate.

One of the recurring themes in animal diversity is body shape. Look at the list of phyla above. Animals have two forms of symmetry, either bilateral (like us) or radial (like sea stars). The exception to this is the sponges (Phylum Porifera) that have neither bilateral nor radial symmetry. Bilaterally symmetric organisms are those that could be cut in half and the halves are mirror images of each other. Part of becoming bilaterally symmetric is a process known as cephalization. As the term implies, this process moves the major sensory structures and their associated nerves towards the head end of the organism. This generally creates a 'brain' within the head of these organisms. In addition, these animals always have particular anatomical features. They always have a head end (anterior) and a tail end (posterior or caudal). They always have a back (dorsal) and front (ventral) surface. Think of a vertebrate, such as a dog, they obviously have a head end, a tail end, a back (dorsal) and a belly (ventral).

Radially symmetric organisms don't have any of these features. They have no head or tail end and generally don't have a back or belly. Organisms like the sea star have a surface that has the mouth, the oral surface, and an aboral surface, without a mouth. Any of the five arms may be the lead arm as it moves across the bottom of the ocean in search of prey. Another common theme among organisms is segmentation. Segmentation divides the body spaces into many small compartments rather than having one large compartment. What is the advantage of this? And it is obviously an advantage when you consider that the most successful group of animals on the face of this earth, Phylum Arthropoda, is segmented. To understand the advantages of segmentation one has to understand the properties of a hydrostatic skeleton. A hydrostatic skeleton is essentially a water-filled chamber that muscles contract around. Since water is incompressible, muscles can use this "skeleton" to cause body movements.

Look at the list of major phyla again and notice that three have "worm" in their common name description. A worm shape, called **vermiform,** is a very common body shape. Look at all the other phyla above. Are there animals in each that could be considered vermiform?

Each of the major phyla has animals with the vermiform body shape. There are finger sponges, coral polyps and hydra, slugs and squid, sea cucumbers, snakes, glass lizards, and weasels. Among the minor phyla are even more worm or tube shaped animals. Examples of minor phyla are Nermertina (ribbon worms), Onychophora (velvet worms), Pogonophora (beard worms), Echiura (spoon worms), and Sipuncula (peanut worms). What are some of the advantages of being vermiform?

If you look at where the vermiform animals live, you get a clue as to why animals may be worm shaped. In addition to increased mobility through soil and mud, physiological mechanisms are enhanced by being worm shaped. Remember that an important aspect of body size and shape is the surface area to volume ratio. A spherical organism has the smallest surface area/volume ratio. If you stretch that organism and make it tubular, the surface area/volume ratio changes significantly.

Examples of vermiform animals:

Lumbricus	Phylum Annelida
Ascaris	Phylum Nematoda
Lolligo	Phylum Mollusca
Cucumaria	Phylum Echinodermata
Garter snake	Phylum Chordata

In the following exercises, you will view illustrations of several vermiform specimens from various phyla.

EXERCISE 20.1. EARTHWORM—*LUMBRICUS* SP.—PHYLUM ANNELIDA

Materials

- Illustrations:

  Earthworm, dorsal

  Earthworm, anterior

  Earthworm, posterior

  Earthworm, external anatomy

  Earthworm (c.s.)

  Earthworm, *Lumbricus terrestris*

Procedure

1. Examine the illustrations of the earthworm (Figures 20.1–20.6) and find the following anatomical positions—dorsal, ventral, anterior, and caudal. The dorsal side is darker and smoother, while the ventral surface is

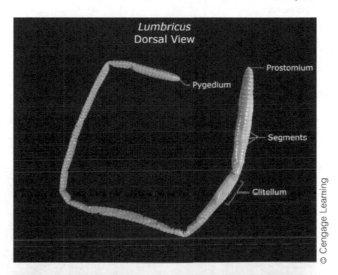

Figure 20.1
Earthworm, dorsal

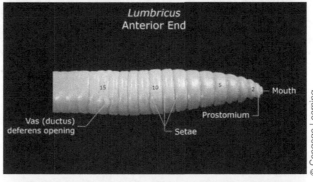

Figure 20.2
Earthworm, anterior

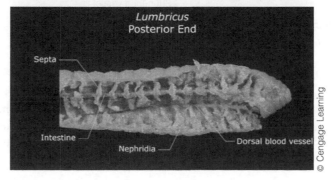

Figure 20.3
Earthworm, posterior

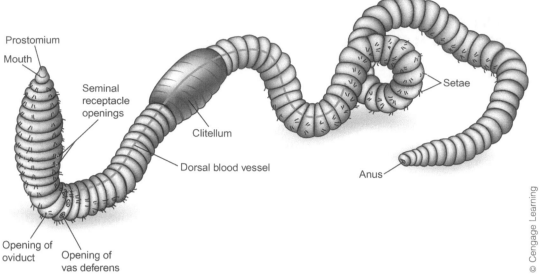

Figure 20.4
Earthworm, external anatomy

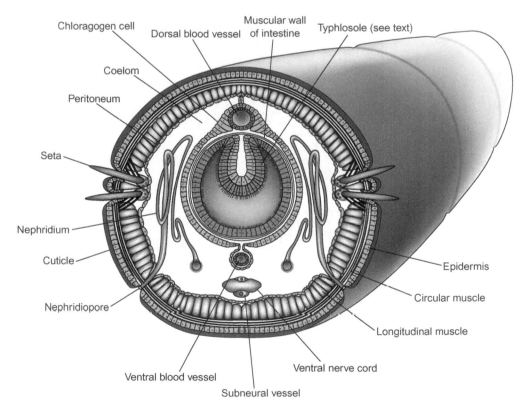

Figure 20.5
Earthworm (c.s.)

lighter and rough-feeling. Bristles or setae (Figure 20.2) that stick out to help the animal move cause the roughness. The anterior or head end of the animal (Prostomium—Figure 20.1) is the end closest to the clitellum and contains the mouth (Figure 20.2). The clitellum (Figure 20.1) is a light-colored, smooth, cylindrical structure. Opposite of the head end is

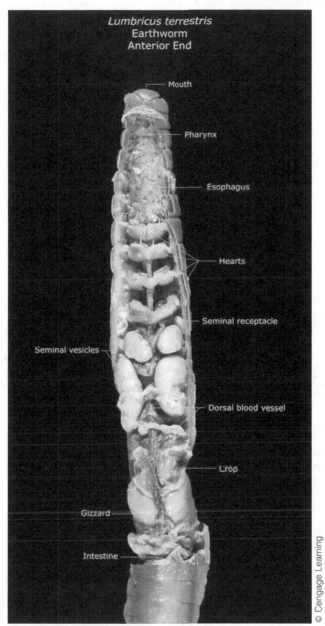

Lumbricus terrestris
Earthworm
Anterior End

— Mouth

— Pharynx

— Esophagus

— Hearts

— Seminal receptacle

Seminal vesicles —

— Dorsal blood vessel

— Crop

Gizzard —

Intestine —

© Cengage Learning

Figure 20.6
Earthworm, lumbricus terrestris

the caudal end (Pygedium—Figure 20.1) that contains the anus. Note the obvious segmentation of this animal (Figures 20.1–20.2).

2. Using the illustrations, find the following:

- **Aortic arches**—five pairs in segments 7–11.
- **Seminal vesicles**—large light colored bodies that contain the sex organs
- **Crop**—thin-walled food storage sac
- **Gizzard**—thick-walled mechanical digestion sac
- **Intestine**—long digestive tube
- **Dorsal blood vessel**—runs on top of digestive tract
- **Protonephridia**—a pair of tubes in each segment except for first three and the last.

- **Cerebral ganglion**—light colored brain in first segment surrounding pharynx
- **Ventral nerve cord**—below intestine—look for segmental ganglia and lateral nerves

EXERCISE 20.2. ROUNDWORM—*ASCARIS SP.*—PHYLUM NEMATODA

Materials

- Illustrations:

    Roundworm, anatomy

    Roundworm (c.s.)

    Ascaris anatomy

    Ascaris male and female

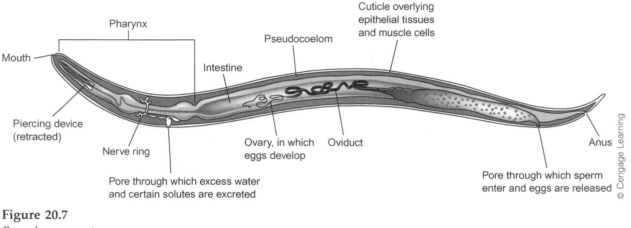

Figure 20.7
Roundworm anatomy

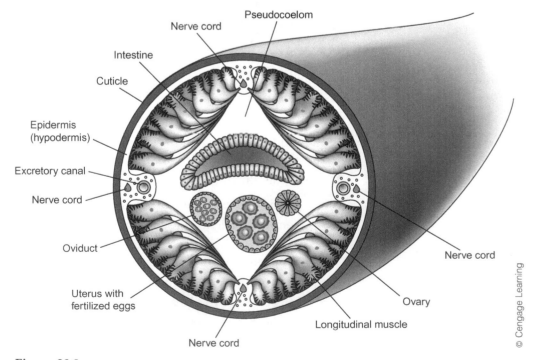

Figure 20.8
Roundworm (c.s.)

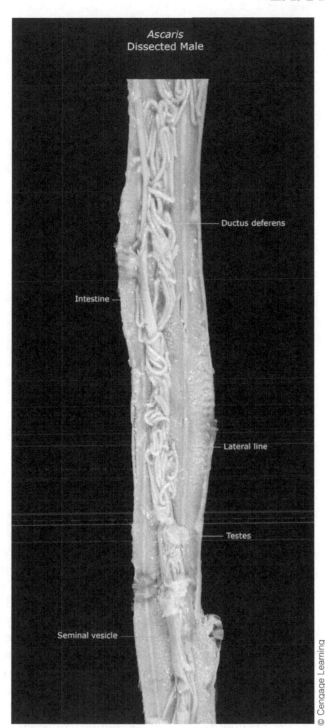

Figure 20.9
Ascaris anatomy

Procedure

1. Using the following illustrations, find the following anatomical positions: dorsal, ventral, anterior, and caudal. Note the lack of segmentation. The body is covered by a thin, transparent acellular layer called the cuticle. This is secreted by the epidermis of the animal and offers some protection from the environment and from predators. Can you

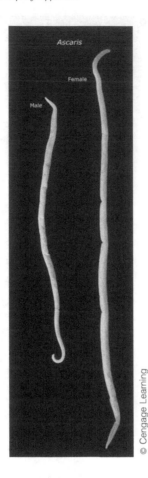

Figure 20.10
Ascaris male and female

distinguish dorsal from ventral? Not very easily. Look for 4 narrow, white lines running from one end of the animal to the other. The thin ones are the longitudinal lines (dorsal and ventral) and the thicker ones are the lateral lines. Which is dorsal and which is ventral? You can determine this once you've examined the internal anatomy. Can you tell the anterior from the caudal end? One end has the mouth and the other has the anus. Again, internal anatomy will help.

2. Notice the lack of internal segmentation. Do you see any parts of the intestinal tract that resemble a crop or a gizzard? The intestine of these animals is just a straight tube from the mouth to the anus. This is primarily because the animals are pseudocoelomates, and don't have the tissue to make muscles that help define different portions of the gut. The tubes that you see in this animal are a complex collection of digestive and reproductive system tubes. The mouth end of this animal has a muscular pharynx in front of the mouth.

EXERCISE 20.3. SQUID—*LOLLIGO* SP.—PHYLUM MOLLUSCA

Materials

- Illustrations:

  Squid anatomical planes

  Squid external anatomy

  Squid anatomy

  Squid-external anatomy anterior

  Squid-external anatomy posterior

Procedure

1. Examine the squid specimen from the illustration. Find the following anatomical positions: dorsal, ventral, anterior, and caudal. Note the overall tubular appearance of the body. Find the funnel, this is the ventral surface.

2. Using the illustrations, find the following:

   - **Arms**—four pairs of equal length arms with suckers along the entire underside

   - **Tentacles**—one pair of long tentacles with suction pads only on the distal ends

   - **Mouth**—located in the center of the arms; note the hard beak

   - **Eyes**—one pair on either side of the head

   - **Funnel**—muscular tube that directs a strong water current allowing the animal to use "jet" propulsion

   - **Mantle**—a thick cone of muscles surrounding the funnel – used to propel water

   - **Coelom**—body space that holds internal organs

   - **Esophagus**—muscular tube that moves food from the mouth to the stomach

   - **Anus** and **rectum**—collection place for feces

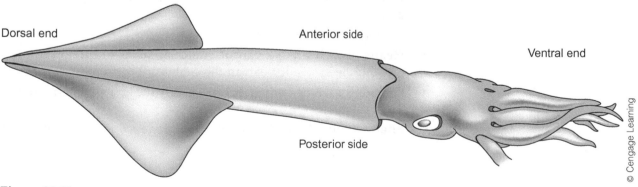

Figure 20.11
Squid anatomical planes

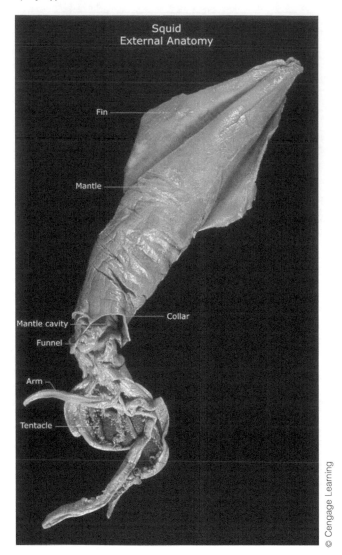

Figure 20.12
Squid external anatomy

- **Intestine**—follows the rectum caudally—where digestion takes place
- **Stomach**—large round organ
- **Hearts**—two hearts—a pair of branchial hearts at the top of each gill and the systemic heart in the center of the body
- **Gonads**—a whitish organ that fills nearly the entire posterior of the body cavity
- **Shell**—a thin "horny" plate of material, dorsal to the body cavity

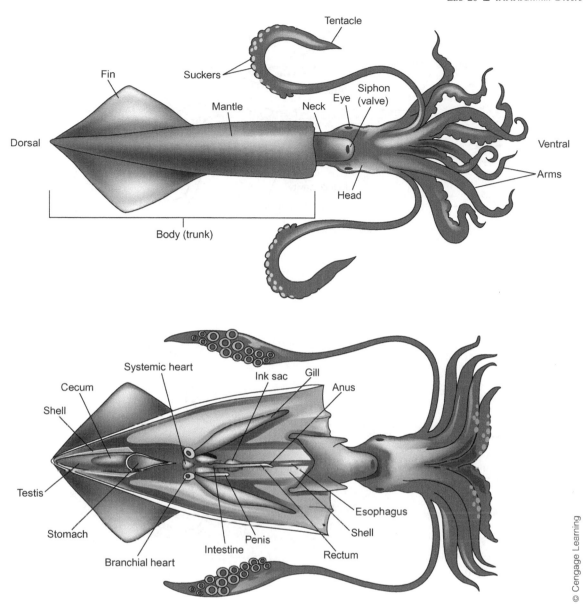

Figure 20.13
Squid anatomy

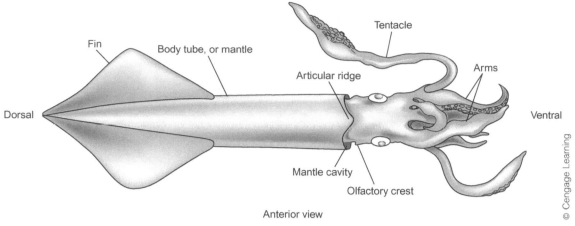

Figure 20.14
Squid-external anatomy anterior

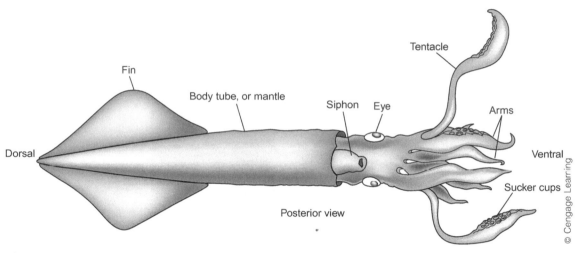

Figure 20.15
Squid-external anatomy posterior

EXERCISE 20.4. SEA CUCUMBER—*CUCUMARIA* SP.—PHYLUM ECHINODERMATA

Materials

- Illustrations:

  Sea cucumber
  Cucumaria frondosa

Procedure

1. Examine the illustrations of the sea cucumber and determine the following anatomical positions: dorsal, ventral, anterior, and caudal. These animals are not like any other animals you have examined. Echinoderms are radially symmetric. Just picture a seastar. The top is the aboral surface, the bottom is the oral surface, and the arms are arranged radially around the center. Sea cucumbers' radial symmetry is obscured with a superimposed bilateral symmetry. The end with the

Figure 20.16
Sea cucumber

© Cengage Learning

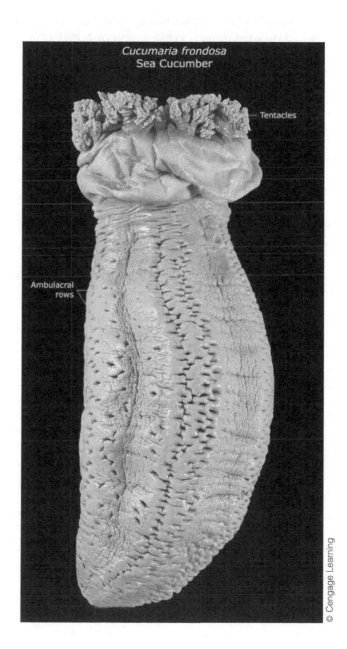

Cucumaria frondosa
Sea Cucumber

Tentacles

Ambulacral
rows

© Cengage Learning

Figure 20.17
Cucumaria frondosa

tentacles, which surround the mouth, is the anterior. The dorsal side has two or three rows of reduced tube feet. The ventral side has two or three rows of long tube feet that are the primary means of locomotion. At the opposite end from the mouth is the caudal end, terminating with a cloacal opening. A cloaca is a body space that contains the product of both the intestines and the reproductive system.

EXERCISE 20.5. SNAKE—*GARTER SNAKE*—PHYLUM CHORDATA

Materials

- Illustration:

  Snake

Procedure

Examine the snake illustration and determine the following anatomical positions: dorsal, ventral, anterior, and caudal. This should be very obvious on a fellow vertebrate.

© Cengage Learning

Figure 20.18
Snake

Assignment 20: Phylum Characteristics

Directions: Answer the following questions regarding phylum characteristics.

1) What are the distinguishing characteristics of each of these phyla?

Annelida

_____

_____

_____

Nematoda

_____

_____

_____

Mollusca

_____

_____

_____

Echinodermata

_____

_____

_____

Chordata

_____

_____

_____

2) After examining the external anatomy of each of these organisms, discuss their similarities?

_____

_____

_____

What's different?_____

_____

www.Investigative Project: Data Compilation and Analysis

This lab is designed for use in distance learning programs.

Prepared by Frank A. Romano III, Benjamin G. Blair, Stacy Blair and William R. Bowen, Jacksonville State University

The following questions are to be answered during this lab. You will need the answers to these questions and the analyses (worksheet titled Assignment 21) performed in this lab to write your report.

- What part of the plant (leaf, stem, or root) was the first to emerge from the seed?
- Did the placement of the seeds in the petri dish alter how each seed germinated, that is, which part emerged first, or how did it grow? Did the parts growing out of the seed all grow in the same direction?
- Did any of the seeds have a different germination time? Did the parts of the germinating plant grow at the same rate?
- What was the rate of growth for the different seeds as they germinated?
- Did the seeds that were planted all grow at the same rate?
- What was the growth rate of each of your plants?

A question that you might pose is, "How do I know if the plants grew differently or not?" This is not such a silly question as it has been asked by scientists the world over. The answer lies in statistical analysis of data. If you can measure differences between the plants and analyze these differences so that they attain statistical significance, then you will know that the plants really did grow differently. To analyze your data, first look at the data you've compiled. Are there obvious differences between the 4 plants that you grew (assuming that they all lived)? If there are, then separate them into appropriate groups and analyze them separately. Compile your data into a form that will be meaningful to your classmates. This should include the final shoot lengths for each plant and the final length of the roots (primary root only). After you have compiled your own data, share it with your classmates. Once you have collected the data, calculate the mean, median, mode, standard deviation, and t-test on root growth and on shoot growth. Be sure to prepare graphs of your data for shoot and root growth.

CENTRAL TENDENCY AND VARIABILITY

You were given eight seeds to grow during the first lab of this semester. You grew four plants in peat disks and four plants in a plastic cup. You were to take daily measurements of plant shoot growth from your plants growing in the peat disks and daily measurements of plant root growth from your plants growing in the plastic cup. Your job now is to analyze your data. By collecting all these data you are trying to estimate the growth, both root and shoot, of this type of plant. To do this with a sample of only four plants is not a very good estimate. Consider the variability that you found within just your four plants and imagine what it might be if you considered several hundred.

Think of it this way. Look at the variability of height, weight, eye, hair, and skin color in a group of just four students within your class. You shouldn't find that much variability and your estimate of the average human and the variability found within humans considering just these four students would not be very reliable. Expand your sample to all the students in your biology lab. Would your estimate be more reliable? Would you get a different average and a different range? Most likely the answer would be yes. Expand your sample to your biology lecture class. Again, your estimate of the average human and the average amount of variability would change and your estimate would better represent the human race. Expand your sample to an event where several thousand people attend, such as graduation, a sporting event, or a concert. Each event would bring a different set of people and your estimate of the average human and the amount of variability would change. This is why a sample of just a few individuals is not very reliable and why you are asked to use the data collected by your group.

It should be obvious to you that you will get a better estimate of the growth of this bean plant by using a larger number of plants. Compare the average and the range found within your four plants to that found in your group's data. You should see a large difference. Remember this when you read reports in newspapers and magazines or hear reports on the radio or television. If the sample is relatively small the reliability of the estimates of an entire population are poor!

BASIC STATISTICS

Large amounts of data are frequently collected in biological studies, as you have found out growing and measuring your plants. The data you collected are a sample of several of the attributes that your plants have. If you include data collected by your fellow students, you're actually sampling a population of plants, not just a few individuals. Sampling data normally has two features of interest: a central tendency and a pattern of variability. Each plant will not grow exactly the same even if they are subjected to identical conditions. What you're interested in is what value best describes the plants, which is the central tendency or average. You'll be able to calculate the average total growth or the average daily growth for your plants. The other measure you might be interested in is how variable is your plant growth? Variability is the range of values measured around the average. You can calculate the range of total plant growth for your individual plants and for the population of plants within your lab and you can calculate the percentage of plants that fall within a certain range of the average. Biologists use statistics to describe the central tendency and variability within our samples. Using these techniques one can state the degree of confidence that can be placed on our estimates of central tendency.

There are three common measures of central tendency used with sampling data. These are the mean, mode, and median. The mean is the arithmetic average of your sample values. The mode is which value within your sample data occurs most frequently. The median is the value that is midway between the range extremes.

If a sample set contains the following measures: 1, 1, 2, 2, 2, 2, 3, 3, 4, and 5. The mean (X) is calculated by taking the sum (Σ) of all the sample measurements (X) and divide by the number of measurements (n); $x = \Sigma X/n$. In this example the sum of the measurements (ΣX) = 25. Divide 25 by the number of measurements (10) and the mean is 2.5. The mode is the value that occurs most frequently. Since 2 occurs four times it is the value that occurs most frequently. Mode = 2. The median is the value half way between the range extremes. Since there are 10 measurements, the value that is halfway between these is the fifth value or 2.

There are many ways to describe variability but the most useful are the standard deviation and the variance. Standard deviation(s) describes the percentage of individuals that fall within specified distances of the mean. Thus, 68.26% of the population will fall within the range of one standard deviation, 95.44% of the population will fall within the range of 2 standard deviations, and 99.72% of the population will fall within the range of 3 standard deviations. The sample variance (s^2) describes the variability within a sample in terms of the deviation (squared) of individual measurements from the mean, divided by the total number of observations (n) minus one ($n - 1$). An easy way of calculating both the standard deviation and variance of the sample is to compute variance using the following formula and taking the square root to determine the standard deviation.

$$s^2 = \frac{\Sigma(X - \bar{X})^2}{n - 1}$$

Where X equals a sample measurement, $\bar{X}$ equals the sample mean and n equals the total number of sample measurements.

Using the sample above create columns as follows.

Sample	Mean	Deviation	Deviation^2
1	2.5	1 − 2.5 = −1.5	$(-1.5)^2 = 2.25$
1	2.5	1 − 2.5 = −1.5	$(-1.5)^2 = 2.25$
2	2.5	2 − 2.5 = −0.5	$(-0.5)^2 = 0.25$
2	2.5	2 − 2.5 = −0.5	$(-0.5)^2 = 0.25$

(Continued)

Sample	Mean	Deviation	Deviation^2
2	2.5	$2 - 2.5 = -0.5$	$(-0.5)^2 = 0.25$
2	2.5	$2 - 2.5 = -0.5$	$(-0.5)^2 = 0.25$
3	2.5	$3 - 2.5 = 0.5$	$(0.5)^2 - 0.25$
4	2.5	$4 - 2.5 = 1.5$	$(1.5)^2 = 2.25$
5	2.5	$5 - 2.5 = 2.5$	$(2.5)^2 = \underline{6.25}$
			Sum = 14.25

$$s^2 = \frac{\Sigma(X - \bar{X})^2}{n - 1} = \frac{14.25}{10 - 1} = \frac{14.25}{9} = 1.58$$

$$s = \sqrt{1.58} = 1.26$$

68.26% of the plants measured should be within the range of $2.5 \pm 1.26 = 3.76 - 1.24$.

In order to test whether your plant grew differently from others one has to enter the data into a statistical test. This will test whether the null hypothesis (that there is no difference between the sample mean and the class mean) should be accepted or rejected. Once this test is completed you can say if the samples were significantly different or not. If you suggest that there is a significant difference or not between two samples that implies that you've done a statistical test. Be sure you understand that when you're writing or talking about science.

To test this we can use a z statistic using the following formula:

$$z = \frac{\bar{X} - \mu}{\sigma_x}$$

Where $\bar{X}$ equals your sample mean and μ equals the class mean, and $\sigma_x = \sigma/\sqrt{n}$.

In others words, the z is the difference between the sample and class means in standard errors of the universe mean. If the difference between the means is small you can assume that the sample mean is likely to be part of, or have come from, the class data. If the difference is great enough (at a particular critical value) you can assume that your data is not part of, or did not come from, the class data. The critical values of z are 1.96 for the 0.05 α level and 2.58 for the 0.01 α level. Calculated z values greater than these suggest that the observed differences could only occur by a change in 5% or 1% of all samplings, respectively. Since these are low probabilities, the null hypothesis is rejected. Thus you can conclude that there are significant differences between your samples and the class samples.

Assignment 21:
Data Compilation and Analysis

Directions: Based on the bean plant data you collected, complete the following tables and graphs.

Now, calculate the mean for both shoot and root growth.

Root Growth Means	Shoot Growth Means

Median: The second measure of central tendency is defined as the value (measurement, count, ratio, etc.) of the middle individual in a series arranged in order of magnitude. In an even-numbered series, the median value will fall midway between the middle two values.

Now order these data for roots and shoots into appropriate series, using the table on the next page; determine the median value.

Mode: The mode is the value within each group attained by the greatest number of plants (used only if large samples are available).

Now determine the mode for each group (from the table above).

Root Growth Modes	Shoot Growth Modes

Now calculate the standard deviation for each group.

Root Growth Standard Deviations	Shoot Growth Standard Deviations

Shoot Length—Plants in Peat		Shoot Length—Plants in Cup		Root Length—Plants in Cup			

Shoot Length— Plants in Peat		*Shoot Length— Plants in Cup*		*Root Length— Plants in Cup*			

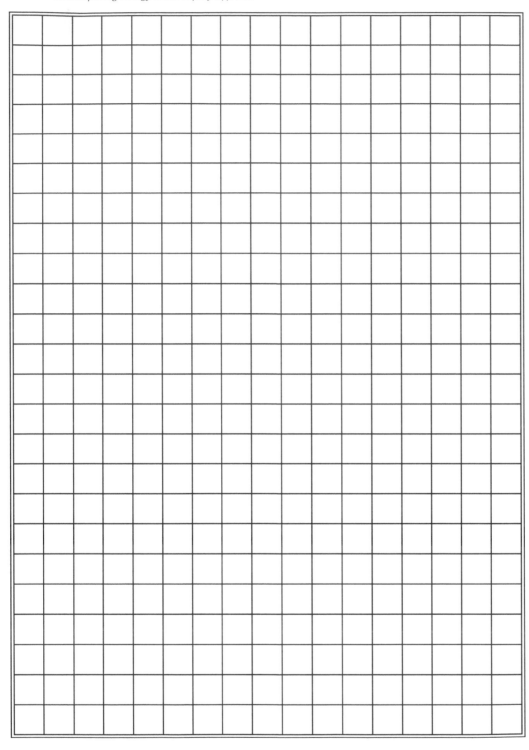

Figure 21.1
Graph of root growth

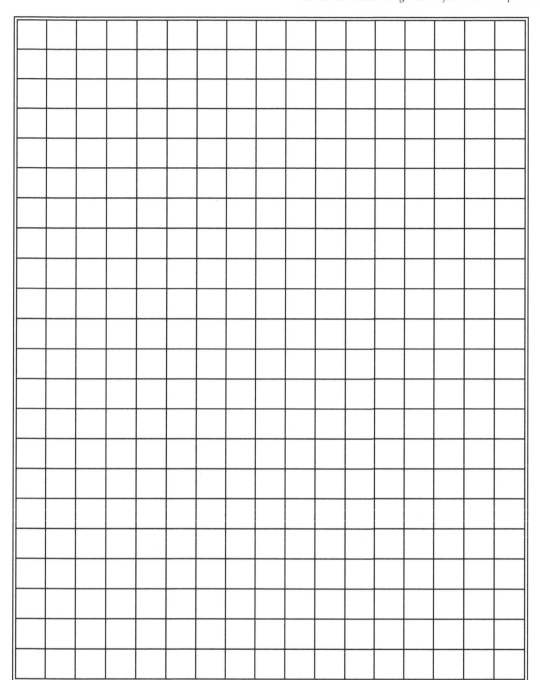

Figure 21.2
Graph of shoot growth

www.Vertebrate Anatomy I and II

This lab is designed for use in distance learning programs.

Prepared by Frank A. Romano III, Benjamin G. Blair, Stacy Blair and William R. Bowen, Jacksonville State University

The pig, *Sus scrofa*, was domesticated by early man and has been living with us for many years. Pigs are members of the same phylum (Chordata), the same subphylum (Vertebrata), and the same class (Mammalia) to which we belong. They, like us, have hair and mammary glands. Pigs are members of a different order (Artiodactyla) which are the even-toed animals. They share this order with cows and deer. Unlike cows and deer, which are ungulates (herbivores) that eat mainly plant material, pigs are omnivores. They will eat both plant and animal matter. Even though pigs are in a different order, nearly all their major structures are the same or very similar in anatomy. In this lab, you will be dissecting a fetal pig. These pigs are not bred for the purpose of dissection, rather they are a by-product of the pork food industry. These animals are purchased from slaughter houses by biological supply companies and are used for scientific purposes rather than being ground up for fertilizer or discarded.

EXERCISE 22.1. FETAL PIG DISSECTION

Materials

- Fetal Pig Anatomy Kit with Dissecting Set
- Examination gloves
- Illustrations and Virtual Pig Dissection (VPD): http://www.glencoe.com/sec/science/cgi-bin/ splitwindow.cgi?top=http://www.glencoe.com/sec/science/ top2.html&link=http://www.whitman.edu/biology/vpd/

  ✔ Please note that before you can view the virtual dissection, you will need to read the requirements for the VPD which will have you to download the latest version of Shockwave Plug-in. You must do this in order to view the dissection. It is a free download and instructions are given as to how to complete the download.

Procedure

1. Your job is to become a pig specialist. Each group of students will be assigned one of the following portions of the pig's organ systems and a list of the organs they should find within each system:

    Group A—External Anatomy and Excretory System: Determine male and female characteristics; learn about and find the **digits, anus, ankle, elbow, mammary papilla, ear, eyelid, shoulder, wrist, umbilical cord, tail, vibrissae,** and **external nares.** Learn about the **kidney, ureter, urethra,** and **urinary bladder.**

    Group B—Respiratory System: Learn about and find the **external nares, internal nares, pharynx, glottis, epiglottis, larynx, trachea, tracheal cartilage, esophagus, bronchus, lung, diaphragm, cranial lobe, caudal lobe, medial lobe, accessory lobe, thoracic cavity, visceral** and **parietal pleura.**

    Group C—Circulatory System: Learn about and find the **heart, pericardial membrane, right ventricle, left ventricle, right atrium, left atrium, superior** and **inferior vena cava, aortic arch, pulmonary artery, pulmonary vein, coronary artery, coronary vein, spleen, renal artery, renal vein, umbilical artery,** and **umbilical vein.**

    Group D—Digestive System: Learn about and find the **oral cavity, hard palate, soft palate, glottis, epiglottis, esophagus, liver, gallbladder, stomach, cardiac** and **pyloric sphincter, pancreas, small intestine, large intestine, tongue, mesentery, duodenum, colon, rectum, abdominal cavity, visceral** and **parietal peritoneum.**

    Group E—Reproductive and Endocrine Systems: Learn about and find the **penis, epididymis, scrotum, spermatic cord, ductus deferens, ovary, oviduct, uterus, horn of the uterus, vagina, urogenital openings.** Learn about and find **thymus, thyroid,** and **adrenal glands.**

2. Before you begin any dissection, please read the *Dissection of the Fetal Pig* laboratory manual thoroughly. Since dissection procedures are different for each sex, be sure you can identify the sex of your fetal pig. In addition to the dissection manual, the above link will aid you in determining the sex of your pig.

3. You, as student learners, are responsible for gathering information, confirming your identifications with the other group members performing the same dissection, and teaching the other members of your class about your assigned system(s) and organs, and their functions. You may use any source of information that you wish, such as lab manuals, the internet, and your textbook. Complete the worksheet titled Assignment 22.1.

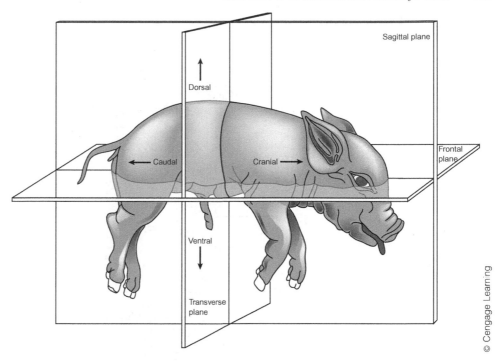

Figure 22.1
Fetal pig planes

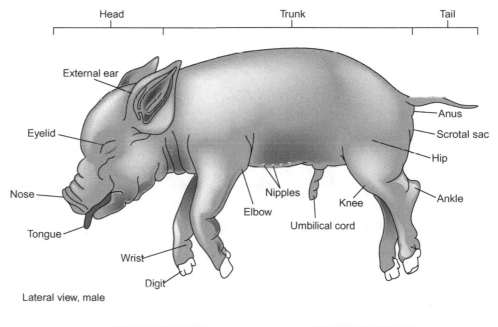

Lateral view, male

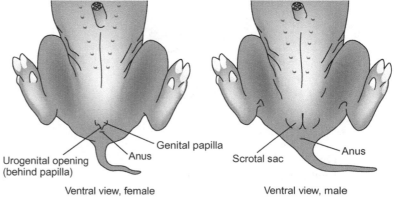

Ventral view, female   Ventral view, male

Figure 22.2
Fetal pig external anatomy

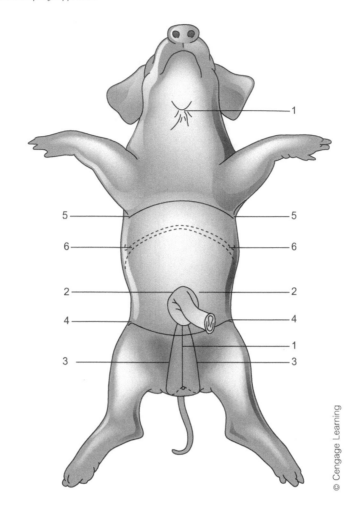

Figure 22.3
Fetal pig incisions

© Cengage Learning

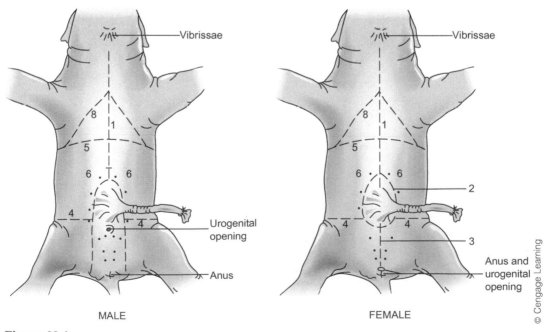

MALE   FEMALE

Figure 22.4
Fetal pig dissection incisions

© Cengage Learning

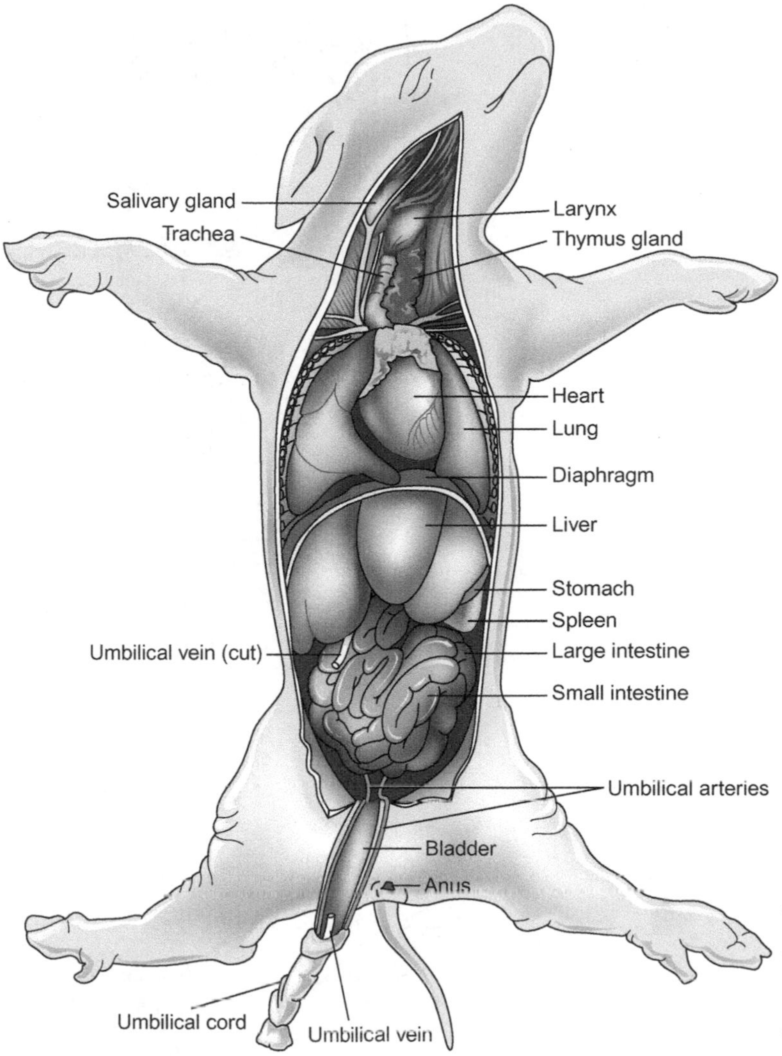

Figure 22.5
Fetal pig superficial dissection

© Cengage Learning

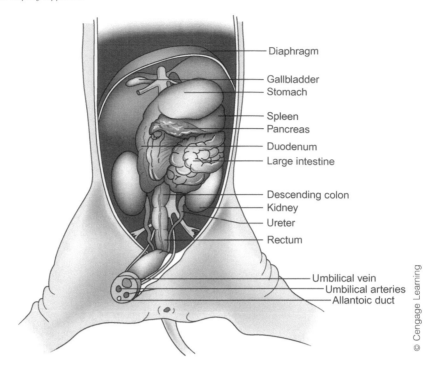

Figure 22.6
Fetal pig deep dissection

Internal Anatomy of Fetal Pig

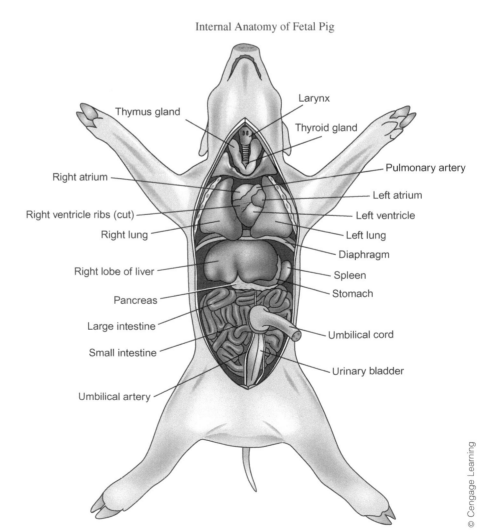

Figure 22.7
Fetal pig internal anatomy

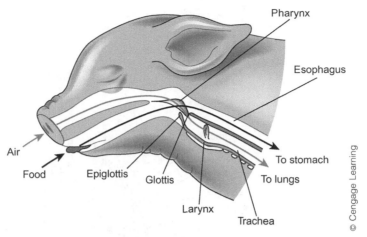

Pharynx

Esophagus

Air

Food

Epiglottis

Glottis

To stomach

To lungs

Larynx

Trachea

© Cengage Learning

Figure 22.8
*Fetal pig airways
and esophagus*

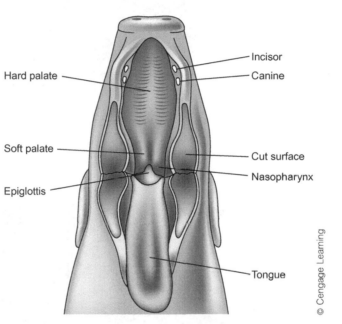

Hard palate

Incisor

Canine

Soft palate

Cut surface

Nasopharynx

Epiglottis

Tongue

© Cengage Learning

Figure 22.9
Fetal pig oral cavity

© 2009 Frank A. Romano III, Benjamin G. Blair, Stacy Blair and William R. Bowen

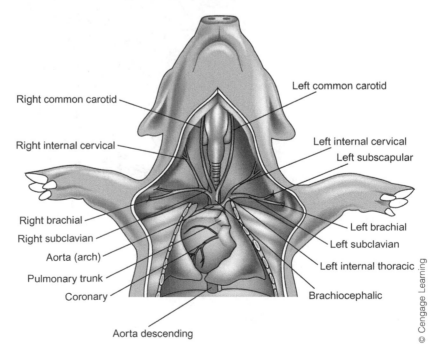

Right common carotid

Left common carotid

Right internal cervical

Left internal cervical

Left subscapular

Right brachial

Right subclavian

Aorta (arch)

Pulmonary trunk

Coronary

Left brachial

Left subclavian

Left internal thoracic

Brachiocephalic

Aorta descending

© Cengage Learning

Figure 22.10
*Fetal pig thoracic and cervical
arteries*

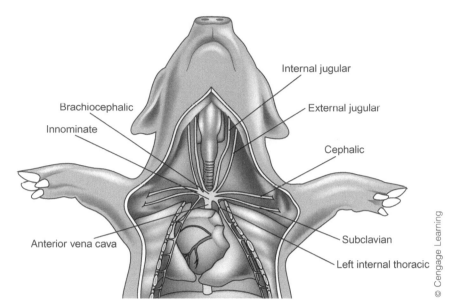

Figure 22.11
Fetal pig thoracic and cervical veins

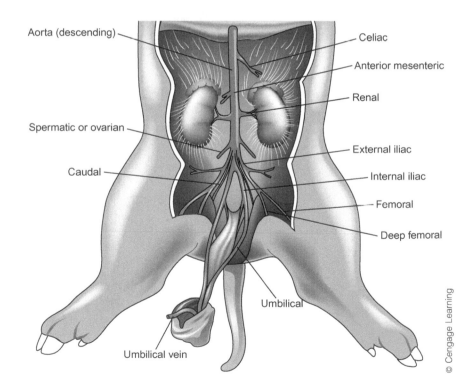

Figure 22.12
Fetal pig abdominal arteries

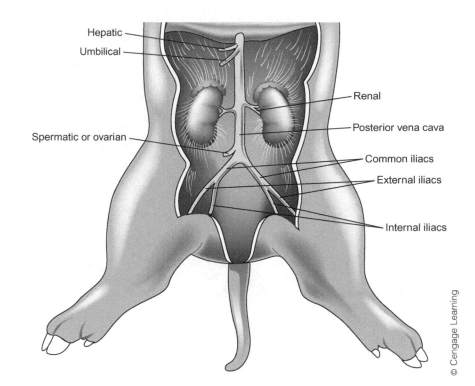

Figure 22.13
Fetal pig abdominal veins

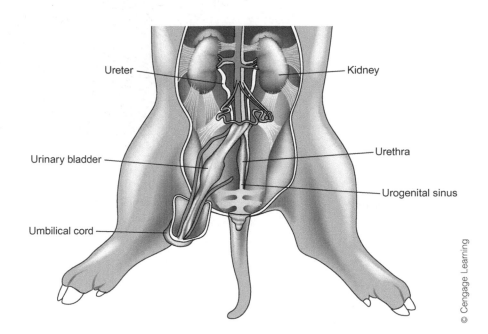

Figure 22.14
Fetal pig urinary system

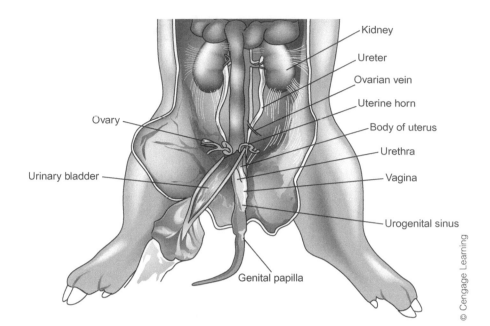

Figure 22.15
Fetal pig female urogenital system

© Cengage Learning

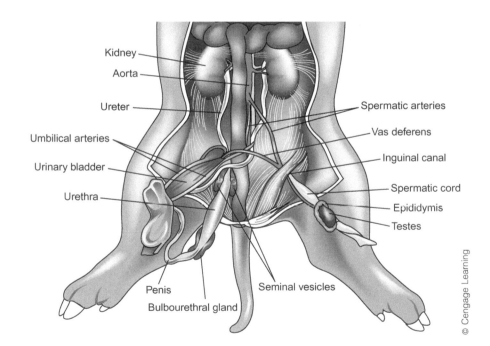

Figure 22.16
Fetal pig male urogenital system

© Cengage Learning

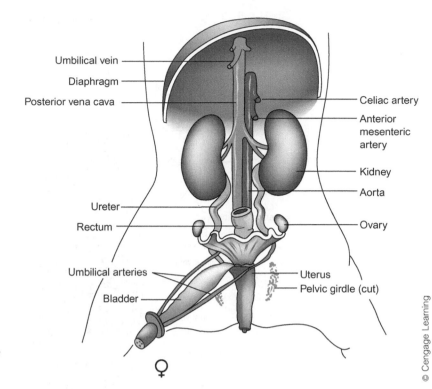

Umbilical vein
Diaphragm
Posterior vena cava
Celiac artery
Anterior mesenteric artery
Kidney
Aorta
Ureter
Rectum
Ovary
Umbilical arteries
Uterus
Pelvic girdle (cut)
Bladder

♀

© Cengage Learning

Figure 22.17
Fetal pig female reproductive system

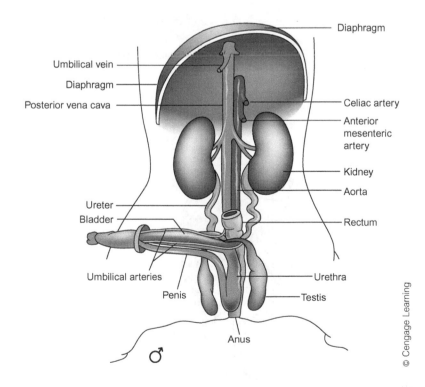

Diaphragm
Umbilical vein
Diaphragm
Posterior vena cava
Celiac artery
Anterior mesenteric artery
Kidney
Aorta
Ureter
Bladder
Rectum
Umbilical arteries
Penis
Urethra
Testis
Anus

♂

© Cengage Learning

Figure 22.18
Fetal pig male reproductive system

Fetal Pig Arteries and Veins

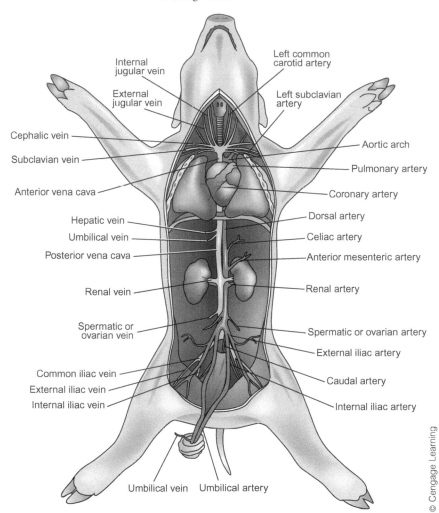

Internal
jugular vein

Left common
carotid artery

External
jugular vein

Left subclavian
artery

Cephalic vein

Aortic arch

Subclavian vein

Pulmonary artery

Anterior vena cava

Coronary artery

Hepatic vein

Dorsal artery

Umbilical vein

Celiac artery

Posterior vena cava

Anterior mesenteric artery

Renal vein

Renal artery

Spermatic or
ovarian vein

Spermatic or ovarian artery

External iliac artery

Common iliac vein

Caudal artery

External iliac vein

Internal iliac artery

Internal iliac vein

Umbilical vein   Umbilical artery

© Cengage Learning

Figure 22.19
Fetal pig arteries and veins

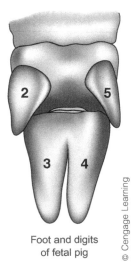

2   5

3   4

Foot and digits
of fetal pig

© Cengage Learning

Figure 22.20
Fetal pig foot and digits

Assignment 22.1: Fetal Pig Dissection

Directions: The following is a list of questions that you are asked (as a group) to research and be prepared to discuss your findings with your classmates.

Fetal Pig Organ System Questions

- Respiratory System—Describe and discuss any changes in the respiratory system that might occur in the fetus just prior to birth? (Note: This is one of the last systems to completely develop and that premature births often require respiratory support.)

- Circulatory System—Describe and discuss what is unique about fetal circulation when compared to the adult? (Note: The first organ to receive oxygenated blood in the fetus is the liver but in the adult it is the heart!)

- Digestive System—Describe and discuss differences between the pig (omnivore) and a herbivorous or carnivorous digestive system?

- Reproductive System—Describe and discuss any changes that might happen to this system as the pig matures?

- Endocrine System—Describe and discuss any changes that might happen to this system as the pig matures?

- External System—Describe and discuss the major differences between males and females? Describe and discuss how this system might change as the pig matures?

- Excretory System—Describe and discuss any changes that might occur in this system as the pig matures?

www.Informed Decision Making I: Issues in Biology

This lab is designed for use in distance learning programs.

Prepared by Frank A. Romano III, Benjamin G. Blair, Stacy Blair and William R. Bowen, Jacksonville State University

OBJECTIVES

❏ Participate in an informed decision making process.
❏ Understand how biological information can be used in a decision making process.

As a citizen and a member of the human race, you will periodically be faced with making an informed decision about an issue that is biologically based. In most instances, that decision will also be an ethical one, for it will test your ability to think without prejudice toward other humans. These issues range from genetic, reproductive, and developmental issues that affect each of us as individuals, to environmental issues that affect us collectively as the human species. Techniques have been developed to assist us, as humans, to deal with the ethical implications of these problems. The technique that will be presented in this lab is one that is based on the assumption that value judgments can be made in a rational and logical manner using non-biased information derived scientifically, rather than by using biased information based on beliefs even though you as an individual may have a strong belief about an issue. Too often we are not consciously aware of the values we hold, and we often make judgments at the emotional level without carefully considering all of the alternatives open to us. The purpose of this exercise is to help you learn to identify your own values more clearly and to apply those values along with scientific data to decisions involving social and environmental issues.

To make a decision is one thing. To make a decision that is ethical and informed is another. When that decision is also societal, impacting not only you, but the rest of our society, it is still another matter. Ethical and informed decisions must be made daily, as our technological society interacts with our environment. The decisions may be personal or they may be populational. As a citizen in our democratic society, you have the right to influence what happens in your local community, as well as in your county, state, and nation. Which should come first: greed or the environment? The decision—right or wrong—is one that impacts all of us and generations to come.

Choices have to be made. Some choices are very difficult and can be highly argumentative. The decisions you make must also be positions that you are able to defend with a clear conscience. For one thing, our society is becoming increasingly technological, and the basis for that technology is science; in fact, technology is applied science. To understand technology, you must first have an understanding of the science that triggered it. Technology today is everywhere, affecting our lives on a daily basis. Technology has spawned genetic engineering, gene therapy, life support technology as well as virtually all of the plants and animals that we use directly and indirectly as food, clothing, sources of drugs, and shelter.

In this exercise, you will become part of a small, interactive group of students that is charged with making and defending an **Informed and Ethical Decision** about an issue—be it biological or environmental. You will need to identify your own personal values—perhaps more clearly than ever before, and apply those values without prejudice to the decision-making process. Will ethical considerations outweigh greed and other factors? Will our emotions prevent us from carefully considering all of the alternatives open to us? The decision-making process will test your ability to think and act without prejudice toward others.

THE SCIENCE AND ART OF MAKING AN INFORMED AND ETHICAL DECISION

During this exercise, you will actively participate as an individual responsible for helping to make a group "informed and ethical decision" about an assigned environmental/biological issue. The protocol will require both individual and group input.

Evaluation. To receive potential full credit for this exercise, the group will submit a report detailing step-by-step how the group arrived at its decision. The degree of participation of each member of the group—from inactive to active—will have a definite impact on your grade for this project.

To arrive at an informed and ethical decision you and your group will use a protocol that has been adapted and modified as a laboratory experience, from the following resources:

1. Creager, Joan G. In *Human Anatomy and Physiology*. Belmont, CA: Wadsworth Publ., a part of Cengage Learning.

2. Kieffer, George H. in *American Biology Teacher* 41(1979): 176.

The experience of participating in the process whereby one makes an informed and ethical decision should enable you to cope with the increasing number of ethical issues that face every member of society on a daily basis.

EXERCISE 24.1. MAKING AN INFORMED AND ETHICAL DECISION

Protocol

Phase I—Initial group planning

1. **Your interactive group**

   An interactive group of four to five students is to be constituted. For this lab, the lab instructor will assign each group member the **same biological or environmental issue**. You will need to interact with your group often and delegate tasks to be performed by each member.

   This effort will require the cooperation of each member. One member should act as the leader or group chair. Another may act as a recorder, recording all discussion and conclusions.

   Every issue requires some background research; that is what informed means. Your group must ascertain how and from where pertinent background information can be obtained. For example, pertinent information may be available from such agencies as the Environmental Protection Agency, the Alabama Department of Environmental Management, the USGA, National Forest Unit or State Forestry Unit, the Natural Resource Conservation Service, the University library, the local community library, the Internet, etc.

   Determine which member of the group will be responsible for acquiring which information from a particular source. You each have the responsibility for completing your assigned task of background research before the stated deadline.

   Your group will then apply the following approach to making an ethical and informed decision on the assigned issue.

Phase II—Individual responsibilities

2. **Becoming *informed* about the issue**

   To make an informed decision, the group must be fully informed about the problem the selected issue represents.

   For example, if your group has the right to abortion as its issue, then background information should be obtained on the following as well as other aspects:

   ✔ How often are abortions performed?

   ✔ At what stage of pregnancy are they usually done?

   ✔ Is race an underlying issue?

   ✔ How much do abortions cost and who pays?

   ✔ Under what circumstances or consequences might be considered positive, negative or neutral?

3. **Deciding on a personal course of action**

   Your most important values are used to select a course of action. By evaluating each issue according to how well it satisfies the needs expressed in your most important values, you should be able to decide on a course of action. That course of action is, of course, your personal "informed and ethical decision." The validity of such a decision can be evaluated by asking yourself if you could live with the decision. If you find that you cannot, try to determine which of your values are in conflict with the decision and modify the decision accordingly.

4. **Determining the consequences of each course of action**

   List all possible consequences of each course of action, regardless of whether the consequences might be considered positive, negative, or neutral. Avoid making a value judgement about any particular consequence.

5. **Developing your personal code of ethics**

   Now assign *your* personal values or ethical considerations to each possible course of action. Each individual has his/her own particular set of personal and/or religious values; therefore, you probably have a positive or negative attitude about each of the courses of action proposed. You can express a problem with the issue as a value statement. Such a personal code of ethics may include:

   ✔ Respect for autonomy, such as the freedom to choose

   ✔ The right of privacy or the right to restrict another's freedom; e.g., the right to life, the right to abortion

   ✔ Beneficence, such as helping others, or abstaining from harming them

   ✔ Justice, such as equal distribution of goods and services to all; equal distribution of goods and services according to individual need; equal distribution of goods according to individual effort, or according to societal contribution

   ✔ Religious beliefs or beliefs according to biblical scriptures (i.e., the Bible)

6. **Order or rank these values in terms of their importance to you**

   Priorities can be assigned to values, according to how important each value is to arriving at an acceptable solution. Rank your list of values regardless of which course of action they concern. Rank your entire list (with regard to the other items) from one (most important) to ten (least important).

Phase III—Final group collaboration

The group must now reconvene. Each member should discuss with the other group members:

• the background research they gathered on the selected issue

• their personal course of action

• their personal values or ethics that influenced their decision

• Then the group must make a collaborative *group ethical and informed decision.*

7. **Deciding on a group course of action**

8. **Deciding on a group code of ethics**

   The decision that the group arrives at is one that, in many instances, will impact more than one individual—the community, the county, the state, the nation, and even the world. The group must recognize the 3 criteria universally applied by ethicists and humanists in testing the validity of a particular ethical value:

   a) **Criterion of emotional comfort**

      Can you live with the decision you reached.

   b) **Criterion of universality**

      Will the result be acceptable if everyone made the same decision in a similar situation?

   c) **Criterion of proportionate good**

      Will the decision result in the greatest good for the most people?

   Armed with each group member's individual code of ethics, the group must now arrive at its collective code of ethics as generated by a consensus. A prioritized list of group principles and a group code of ethics should be generated.

   As in any situation that requires a group consensus, you may find yourself unable to persuade other members of the group to accept your solution. Identify tradeoffs that you would be willing to make. For example, if your solution is compatible with all the values on your prioritized list, you may be able to accept a solution that is not consistent with the ninth or tenth place values on your list. Be prepared to accept solutions that sacrifice your least important values in order to retain those values you find most important.

9. **The ethical and informed decision**

   Now the group is in a position to make an informed decision based on sound, ethical principles.

   Write your group's decision in a concise, well-stated manner.

10. **Report—the group's informed and ethical decision**

    The group must now collaborate on writing a report outlining its decision-making process. The report should include:

    ✔ An appropriate title, with all group members clearly identified

    ✔ An introduction to the selected issue, including a defining statement

    ✔ Pertinent information derived from background research

    ✔ A list of terms and definitions agreed upon by your group

    ✔ Your group's code of ethics with a prioritized list of ethical principles, including any reprioritization of ethical principles

    ✔ A prioritized list of possible courses of action and their consequences, including any reprioritization of courses of action

    ✔ The final course of action agreed upon by the group

    If one or more members of the group have arrived at a different decision than the group as a whole, he/she may express that decision and the values/factors leading to it in a minority report.

www.Informed Decision Making II: Environmental Impact

This lab is designed for use in distance learning programs.

Prepared by Frank A. Romano III, Benjamin G. Blair, Stacy Blair
and William R. Bowen, Jacksonville State University

In this laboratory, each group member will playact a part of an Environmental Impact Statement Hearing. This hearing will decide whether the project in question will be allowed to proceed or not. Each group will be either a proponent for or an opponent against the proposed project. The following is the protocol or procedure by which you should logically arrive at an "informed decision" regarding this issue:

An **Environmental Impact Statement** (EIS) is a document that impartially analyzes the significant environmental effects (all socioeconomic and biophysical effects) of a proposed action (project) and how those effects can be avoided or minimized (mitigated). The EIS responds to the substantive issues identified during the public review period. The EIS's purpose is to give early consideration to environmental factors and thus help balance environmental concerns with economic and other social issues.

The major functions of an EIS are to:

- Consider all relevant adverse environmental impacts of a proposed action.
- Discuss measures to reduce/avoid identified adverse impacts.
- Assess a range of reasonable alternatives to the proposed action including the **no action** alternative. The no action alternative details what might happen if the proposal is not implemented.

The culmination of the EIS review process is a "findings statement" prepared by the agency that runs the EIS hearing. It is a written document that says the environmental review requirements have been sufficiently met for a decision to be made on the proposed action; further, a findings decision is made. This decision may be:

- A positive findings statement. That means that the proposed action is approved after the final EIS is reviewed and that the action chosen is the one that minimizes environmental impacts to the maximum extent practicable.
- A negative findings statement. That means that the proposed action is not approved after the final EIS is reviewed. The reasons for denial must be documented.

Each group will role-play the part of some agency or public interest "advocacy" group in a mock hearing on an EIS. The roles to be played are:

✔   Applicant (whose EIS will be used in this mock hearing)

✔   Village/Town/City planning or environmental board/department

✔   Regional Planning Centers

✔   Village/Town/City Community Development Division

✔   ADEM (such as Alabama Department of Environmental Management)

✔   "Citizen's for" Group (such as Businessmen's Association or Developer, Inc.)

✔   "Citizen's against" Group (such as neighbors or taxpayers united)

✔   County/State Health Department

✔   Alabama Conservancy

✔   League of Women Voters

✔   Sportmen's Group (such as Ducks Unlimited, Bassmasters)

✔   Environmental Group (such as Greenpeace, Friends of the Earth)

✔   Small Business Development Center

The object of all persons present at a public hearing is to influence the "findings statement" that will be written by the hearing officer. Perhaps your approach within your role could be to:

1) Decide upon your role's basic position and concerns relative to the proposed project;

2) Review the scoping and permit criteria;

3) Find the EIS inadequacies (if any) and offer additional data/interpretations with regard to the above;

4) Offer comments, data interpretation, or additional alternatives that meet your role's concerns.

Remember that this public hearing is both a critique of the EIS and an attempt to influence the findings statement and permit decision. Interested agencies and individuals can be most effective in presenting their concerns about a proposed project by:

1. knowing the procedures for complying with the environmental regulation, including terminology, time-tables, and the requirements for making a decision;

2. reviewing the EIS, scoping requirements, scientific concepts and terminology, and data interpretation (including scientific and those from other disciplines);

3. focusing on the major issues and/or deficiencies rather than minor discrepancies and wording. The lead agency is only required to consider substantive comments, not speculative or unsupported assertions;

4. organizing comments by placing the most important concerns first;

5. identifying reasonable alternatives and mitigations to reduce or eliminate impacts that may have been overlooked; and

6. highlighting the effects the project may have on the local community, region, or a specific agency program. This could include effects on

community services, housing, land use, transportation, aesthetics, cultural values, or historic resources.

A "mitigation" means to make something less severe or even to produce a beneficial impact. Some typical mitigation measures include:

- screening, landscaping plants to improve degraded landscapes and vistas, and other forms of landscaping (such as lawns to improve water recharge to aquifers);

- reclamation and restoration (such as using waste for land reclamation or reseeding);

- careful timing to minimize plankton blooms, avoiding fish spawns, animal and plant reproduction, or to minimize noise impacts;

- monitoring air/water impacts during construction and during certain periods of operation; and

- construction considerations, such as sedimentation, erosion, siltation, dust control, minimizing land clearing, clustering of structures to reduce the area of impact, and preserving open space and traffic mitigations.

Consider the following EIS summary and application for a sewage treatment facility upgrade and a permit to build a new plant in Jacksonville, AL.

EIS SUMMARY OF ENVIRONMENTAL CONSIDERATIONS

Existing Environmental Conditions

The existing environmental conditions of the 201 planning area have been documented in Section IV. It is concluded that this project would not be detrimental to the existing environment, but would upgrade the receiving waters through improved wastewater treatment.

Future Environment without the Project

If no action is taken to meet the required effluent standards established for the Jacksonville treatment facilities, continued pollution of the receiving waters and its tributaries will occur and water quality will be degraded. The specific effects of "No Action" upon the environment have been documented in Section V.

Evaluation of Alternatives

Each of the alternatives has been assessed for its environmental impacts (see Section VI). It was concluded that no significant adverse effect on the environment would occur from implementation of any of the alternatives.

Environmental Assessment and Considerations

A. Probable impact of the project on environment

The existing wastewater treatment facilities are not adequately designed to meet treatment requirements under peak flow. To protect the fish and aquatic life of the receiving waters and to provide expansion for the city, it is mandatory to make additions to the wastewater treatment and collection system. The proposed wastewater treatment facilities will be designed to attain the effluent limits documented earlier in this report. This should represent a control of pollutants and should result in improvement of water quality. Degradation of the receiving waters should not be significant due to the effluent discharge.

If not properly operated and maintained, the proposed treatment facility could result in the occasional release of some odors. The proposed facilities will be designed to limit and reduce these odors. An Operations and Maintenance Manual will be prepared to describe in detail the methods of reducing/eliminating these odors.

Health hazards resulting from malfunctioning septic tanks can be eliminated as sewers are installed. Possibilities of groundwater contamination should be eliminated. Any pumping station will be designed with no overflows and with auxiliary (standby) power so that the environment will be protected against untreated overflows. No detrimental environmental effects are to be expected from sludge handling and disposal.

The area to be utilized for the proposed treatment plant apparently supports no sensitive ecosystem. The treatment system should not create a significant environmental degradation to this immediate area.

Consideration must be given to the effect on air quality of the increased availability of sewers in the presently undeveloped areas. Slightly higher population densities will probably bring a few more improved roads and additional motor vehicles. An overall decrease in air quality is not expected to occur, especially since the air quality in the project area is not marginal. Portions of the proposed sewers will service or must traverse undeveloped or sparsely developed areas. However, a change in land use in these areas is not expected to be induced by these proposed sewers. Most of the areas are zoned "residential" and there is no reason to believe this classification will change. A sewage collection system tends to increase residential densities because of smaller home sites and the use of multiple-dwelling unit structures. Scattered development in the "fringe" portions of the 201 Planning Area has been encouraged by the lack of suitable sanitary treatment facilities. Any future growth due to this project adjacent to existing development will most likely slightly reduce energy needs for transportation into the immediate area when compared with scattered dwellings.

Aesthetics is an elusive quality, difficult to evaluate and virtually impossible to value. However, aesthetics is a very essential part of a quality environment and society has become increasingly critical of those actions which will erode that quality in any way. All attempts will be made to enhance the appearance of the proposed facilities, including planting of trees for buffer zones, regular maintenance of grounds and fences, a graded access road, etc. A public relations program will be recommended to acquaint the general population with the treatment facilities and the theory of operation.

As discussed in the environmental inventory, no significant historical or archaeological sites have been identified in the 201 Planning Area that would be affected by this project. The proposed project should have no detrimental effect upon existing wildlife within the area. Quite conversely, it may very well improve water habitats.

The Alabama Department of Environmental Management has been contacted and a list of parties available for conducting archaeological surveys has been supplied. Any detailed surveys required will be conducted during Step II Design following field locations of the proposed lines and prior to disturbance of the ground. Should these surveys reveal any significant findings in conflict with the proposed routes, the line locations will be re-evaluated and a determination will be made of appropriate steps, if any, to mitigate possible impacts on significant sites. It is requested that this approach be approved by the various reviewing agencies so that A-95 approval can be obtained. The costs of the surveys are EPA grant eligible and will be included in the Step II application.

The project should not significantly change the botanical or zoological composition of the area nor endanger the existence of any individual species. The project should not significantly affect any rare or endangered species. Higher dissolved oxygen levels should result immediately downstream from the effluent discharge and should enhance the aquatic environment. Any detailed vegetative surveys required will be conducted during Step II Design near all proposed sewer lines by a trained forester or terrestrial biologist except along areas that have been recently cleared. A map will be provided showing major community types, unique communities, and rare or unusual specimens. Attempts will be made to identify habitats that are uniquely suited to rare or endangered species. It is requested that this approach be approved by the various reviewing agencies so that A-95 approval can be obtained. As above, the costs of the survey are EPA grant eligible and will be included in the Step II application.

In general, the following impacts are expected:

A. Improved quality aspects of water, land, and air

  1. Improved waste disposal

  2. Improved stream water quality

B. Improvement, protection and preservation of areas of natural beauty for man's enjoyment

C. Enhancement or preservation of biological resources

  1. Improved quality and increased quantity of fish and wildlife habitat

  2. Protection of rare and endangered species of flora and fauna

B. Any probable adverse environmental effects which cannot be avoided

The easements for the sewer lines and force mains will be in the city streets and easements provided for in the subdivisions. The sites for any lift stations will be obtained after final design is made. The sites will be purchased by the City after field surveys and plats are drawn.

Associated with the construction of the proposed project will be a certain amount of unavoidable damage. Primarily, this will consist of the loss of a small amount of vegetation and some trees inside the construction easements. The construction contractor will be required to return the construction area to preconstruction status where possible. Disturbed areas will be resown or sodded with grasses or with other ground covers that will hold the soil. The environment will be protected from soil erosion and water and air pollution during construction. Contractors will be required to adhere to strict guidelines set forth in each construction contract to minimize soil erosion and water and air pollution during construction. Excavation and construction operations will be scheduled and controlled to prevent exposure of excessive amounts of unprotected soil to erosion and the resulting translocation of sediment. Measures to control erosion will be uniquely specified at each work site and will include, as applicable, use of temporary vegetation or mulches, diversions, mechanical retardation of runoff, and traps.

Motors of construction equipment will be required to have mufflers to reduce noise. Harmful dust and other pollutants inherent to the construction process will be held to minimum practical limits. Haul roads and excavation areas and other work sites will be sprinkled with water as needed to keep dust within tolerable limits.

Contract specifications will require that fuel, lubricants, and chemicals be adequately labeled and stored safely in protected areas, and disposal at work sites will be by approved methods and procedures. Clearing and disposal of brush and vegetation will be carried out in accordance with applicable laws, ordinances, and regulations in respect to burning. Each contract will set forth specific stipulations to prevent uncontrolled grass or brush fires. Disposal of brush and vegetation will be by burying, hauling to approved off-site locations, or by controlled burning, as applicable.

Necessary sanitary facilities will be located to prohibit such facilities being injuriously adjacent to live streams, wells, or springs in conformance with federal, state, and local water pollution control regulations. Conformance to all environmental control requirements will be monitored constantly by a construction inspector who will be on-site during all periods of construction operation.

Construction specifications will restrict the use of heavy construction machinery during very early morning hours in the vicinity of residential areas. Any required blasting or drilling operations will also be confined to certain time intervals and will be done in a manner to minimize any impact on adjacent property.

Some temporary adverse conditions will necessarily result. Generally, these conditions are related to noise from operation of the construction equipment, torn-up streets, and some unavoidable siltation. These conditions will be eliminated upon completion of construction.

In that no wastewater treatment process will completely remove all pollutants, the treated effluent will contain a small amount of biodegradable matter. The residuals will be within accepted levels in that the required treatment limits will be met. Since the degree of treatment with the proposed improvements will be higher than presently exists, the adverse effects of continued discharge to surface waters is considered to be negligible.

C. Relationship between short-term uses of the environment and maintenance of long-term productivity

The improvement of ground and surface waters cannot readily be measured in economic terms, nor can a cost be established for the future recreational possibilities associated with improvements in water quality. However, current and future requirements of the Alabama Department of Environmental Management indicate that improvements in wastewater treatment must be made to provide good water quality for long-term productivity. The primary means of accomplishing improved water quality in the area is the development of the proposed sewerage facilities in the 201 planning area.

There is no anticipated disruption of local short-term uses of the environment (land use, recreation, fish and wildlife, water use) as a result of enhancement of long-term productivity, i.e., providing a long-term solution to public health problems with minimum acceptable degradation to water quality. The project since its inception has been designed to insure maintenance and enhancement of long-term productivity.

Since the inception of this project input has been received from various agencies and organizations concerned with long-term productivity in the area. The standard A-95 Clearinghouse review process is being followed and the comments of all agencies are being incorporated in the development of the project.

D. Any irreversible and irretrievable commitment of resources

Irreversible and irretrievable resources committed to this project are the land and construction materials used for actual facility location, the capital required to finance the project, and chemicals, materials, energy and manpower consumed during routine operation of the facilities. Water resources are committed in that the receiving waters will possibly experience a slight degradation in quality due to the wastewater components remaining after treatment. This commitment, however, is not totally irreversible.

The commitment to growth is virtually irreversible once the sewers are installed. The growth of residential, commercial and industrial areas should be heavily oriented to the available facilities.

No displacement of population will be required by this project.

E. Reasons for concluding there will be no significant impacts

It is concluded that the proposed project will not result in significant environmental impact for the following reasons:

A. The project is not controversial.

B. The EPA's decision on the project will not have national significance.

C. The project will not conflict with or deface residential areas or naturally scenic areas.

D. There are no areas of historical or archaeological significance involved.

E. There are no public parks or lands involved.

F. Present water quality should be upgraded.

G. There is no displacement of population.

H. The project does not involve directly the following:

1. management, protection, or enhancement of areas of national beauty;
2. management, preservation, or enhancement of especially valuable biological resources and ecosystems; or
3. management, preservation, or enhancement of especially valuable geological, archeological and historical resources.

Alabama Department of Environmental Management
State pollutant Discharge Elimination System (SPDES)

MUNICIPAL PERMIT APPLICATION 'FORM A'

Answer All Questions. Where not applicable, enter "N/A."

1. Name of municipality or sewer district *City of Jacksonville* If this is for renewal or modification of a NPDES or SPDES Permit, complete the following:

   Permit No. AL **0020656**   Effective Date *10/1/08*
                                               Expiration Date *10/1/11*

   Refer all correspondence to: (Name, Title and Address)
       Dr. Frank A. Romano,
         Biology Department
         Jacksonville State University
   Telephone No. (*256*) *782-5038*

2. Is part or all of your discharge into a municipal transport system under another responsible organization? YES _____ NO __X__

   (If yes, explain in the additional information section. Give names and address of the organization, the name of the plant receiving the flow, and the amount of flow).

Facility Information—

3. **A.** Location:
   No. and Street *Route 204, Box 27*
   City, Village or Town *Jacksonville, AL*
   County _____*Calhoun*_____
   Latitude: Degree _33_   Minute _49_   Seconds _30_
   Longitude: Degree _85_   Minute _47_   Seconds _00_

   B. Mailing Address (if same as A, indicate):
   No. and Street_*same as above*_____
   City, Village or Town_____
   County_____

   C. Describe Treatment Process—
   primary and advanced secondary

   D. Plant Design Data—
   Flow (MGD): *2.0 MGD (max)*
   Year Plant Began Operation _____1955_
   Year of Latest Plant Revision _____1972_

   BOD_5. _30 day mean_ Influent _79.5_ mg/l; Effluent _14.9_ mg/l _81%_ Removal

   S.S._____ Influent _48.0_ mg/l; Effluent _11_ mg/l _77.5%_ Removal

   N.O.D._____ Influent_____mg/l;   Effluent_____mg/l _____% Removal

   Phosphorus (as P) Influent_____mg/l; Effluent_____mg/l _____% Removal

(BOD$_5$—Biological Oxygen Demand tested for 5 days. Put a water sample into a closed container in the dark and measure the amount of oxygen consumed by the organisms contained in the water. This gives a measure of the amount of organisms and the amount of organic pollution contained in the water. A high reading indicates lots of organisms feeding on lots of organic nutrients; a low reading indicates the opposite.)

(S.S.—Suspended Solids. This gives a measure of the amount of particulate materials found in water. The higher this number is, the more spoiled the water.)

4. E. Plant Schematic—

   Include a plant schematic as an attachment to this application, divide the schematic into wastewater treatment and sludge treatment. Where are sludge and grit ultimately disposed?

   Sludge _given to local homeowners or trucked to a landfill_

   Grit _same as above_

Outfall Information—

5. A. Location:
   No. and Street _same as above (question #3)_
   City, Village or Town_____
   County_____
   Latitude: Degree_____ Minute _____ Seconds _____
   Longitude: Degree_____ Minute _____ Seconds _____

   B. Type Discharge—
   Surface Water _X Williams branch of the Little Tallashatchee creek_
   Ground Water _____
   Other _____ Explain

   C. Receiving Water or Nearest Surface Water—
   Name _X-Williams branch of the Little Tallashatchee creek_
   Classification _B_
   (B-means that the creek is a second order stream, that is, it is formed by two smaller streams coming together to form this larger stream.)

Collection System Information—

6. A. Type—Separate __X__ Combined_____ Both _____
   B. Length ___49.13___ Miles
   C. Service Area—

Municipalities Served	Population
Jacksonville and	9,900
nearby areas	5,400

Total Population 15,300

D. Average daily industrial waste to be received in the collection system _0.2_ MGD (million gallons daily)

E. Are there any Significant Industrial Users? YES __X__ NO_____
[If yes, specify number tributary to plant_____, and complete a question 13 form (page 168) for each industry].

*Refer to Attachment A for definition of a Significant Industrial User.

7. If this is for a permit renewal, describe actions taken to comply with the compliance schedule in your present permit. (Refer to Section C—Special Conditions). *NA*

8. Have you applied for or received a grant for the construction of a wastewater treatment facility? YES __X__ NO_____

If yes, describe *The upgrade of the sewage treatment plant to handle an increased population is to be funded by a federal grant. In addition to this, the city of Jacksonville wished to attract Armstrong Recycling, a lead battery recycling facility that will employ 60 people, and Allan and Muir's Tire Recyclers, a tire recycling facility that will employ 35 people. The city is seeking federal Cleanwater Act funds to help fund this doubling of the sewage treatment plant capacity.*

Date of application or grant award _5/1/04_

9. Will your plant be phased out with your collection system becoming tributary to another publicly owed treatment works?

    YES_____   NO ___X___ If yes, which treatment works?
    _____

    Expected date of discontinuance of discharge _NA_

Discharge Information—

10. A. Check the space next to parameter if it is present:

___ Algicides	___ Chloride	___ Mercury	___ Silver
___ Aluminum	___ Chlorinated Organics	___ Molybdenum	___ Sulfide
___ Antimony	___ Chromium	___ Nickel	___ Surfactants
___ Arsenic	___ Cobalt	_X_ Oil and Grease	___ Thallium
___ Barium	___ Copper	___ Pesticides	___ Tin
___ Beryllium	___ Fluoride	___ Phenols	___ Titanium
___ Boron	___ Iron	___ P.C.B.'s	___ Zinc
___ Bromide	_X_ Lead	___ Radioactivity	
_X_ Cadmium	___ Manganese	___ Selenium	

11. B. Plant Performance Data—(see next page)

12. Overflow and Bypass Information:

Complete a set of questions for each discharge. Include pump station overflows and frequently occurring sewer surcharges which either run overland to the stream or are relieve pumped to the stream. Use additional pages if necessary.

Type:
Outfall No. __001__ Overflow __X__ Bypass_____

Facility Location:
Street __*Route 204*__ City __*Jacksonville*__ County ____*Calhoun*____
Latitude Deg. __33__ Min. __49__ Sec. __30__
Longitude Deg. __85__ Min. __47__ Sec. __00__

Receiving Water:
Name Williams branch of Little Tallashatchee Creek
Class _____B_____
Frequency of Occurrence____ *1–2 times per month Avg.*
Duration of Discharge _____ *8–16 hrs.*
Is treatment provided? YES __X__ NO____ If yes, describe *treatment is provided until disruption of the biological community digester*

13. Significant Industrial Users*—Submit a separate Item 13 page for each significant industry discharging to the municipal system.

A. Name *Armstrong Recylers*
Address ____ *42 Industrial Blvd., Jacksonville, AL*
Telephone No. ____ *(256) 435-0001*

B. Brief description of industry *Recycles lead and acid from automobile batteries*

C. Standard Industrial Classification Code 00001A

(These may be obtained from the 1972 edition of the "Standard Industrial Classification Manual" available from the Government Printing Office, Washington, D.C. A copy of this book is available for inspection at ADEM, Montgomery, AL).

D. Principal Product or Raw Material—

(Specify the principal product and/or principal raw material and the maximum quantity per day produced or consumed. Quantities are to be reported in the units of measurement given in attachment A if that particular SIC Code is listed. Other SIC categories should use the units of measurement normally used by that industry).

Principal Product

Product	Amount per Day	Raw Material	Amount per Day
Recycled Lead	*20,000–30,000 lbs*	*old batteries*	*2,000–3,000*
Recycled acid	*1,000 gallons*	*old batteries*	*2,000–3,000*
_____	_____	_____	_____
_____	_____	_____	_____
_____	_____	_____	_____

E. Flow *200,000 Gallons water per day to sewage treatment plant*

F. Is pretreatment provided? YES ⨯ NO_____ If yes, explain_____
of the soluble lead that enters the water, about 4.39 lbs of the 4.4 lbs. lead per day is recovered by a patented reverse osmosis filter; all sulfuric acid is neutralized on site before sending to the sewage treatment plant.

G. Characteristics of Wastewater—

(Indicate the characteristics of the wastewater from the industry in terms of parameters that will adequately identify the waste such as BOD, COD, Cr, Zn, pH, etc. These should be measured after any pretreatment provided by the industry but prior to entering the municipal system).

Parameter	Concentration Value (units)	Type of Sample Grab or Composite	Number of Samples per Day
Lead	0.01 lb.	Grab	2
Sulfuric Acid	0.0 mg/l	Grab	2

14. Significant Industrial Users*—Submit a separate Item 13 page for each significant industry discharging to the municipal system.

A. Name ___*Allan and Muir's Tire Recyclers*___
Address ____*45 Industrial Blvd., Jacksonville, AL*____
Telephone No. __*(256) 435-1001*__

B. Brief description of industry *Recycles rubber tires*

C. Standard Industrial Classification Code *00001A*

(These may be obtained from the 1972 edition of the "Standard Industrial Classification Manual" available from the Government Printing Office, Washington, D. C. A copy of this book is available for inspection at ADEM, Montgomery, AL).

D. Principal Product or Raw Material—

(Specify the principal product and/or principal raw material and the maximum quantity per day produced or consumed. Quantities are to be reported in the units of measurement given in attachment A if that particular SIC Code is listed. Other SIC categories should use the units of measurement normally used by that industry).

Principal Product

Product	Amount per Day	Raw Material	Amount per Day
Shredded tires	*100,000 pounds*	*used tires*	*10,000*

E. Flow *20,000 Gallons per day water to sewage treatment plant*

F. Is pretreatment provided? YES _____ NO <u> X </u>. If yes, explain___

G. Characteristics of Wastewater—

(Indicate the characteristics of the wastewater from the industry in terms of parameters that will adequately identify the waste such as BOD, COD, Cr, Zn, pH, etc. These should be measured after any pretreatment provided by the industry but prior to entering the municipal system).

15. Additional Information:

      Item   Information

SIGNATURE (must be signed by either a principal executive officer, ranking elected official or other duly authorized entity).

I hereby affirm under penalty of perjury that information provided on this form and any attached supplemental forms is true to the best of my knowledge and belief. False statements made herein are punishable as a Class A misdemeanor pursuant to Section 210.45 of the Penal Law.

_____

Applicant's Signature   Date

_____

Printed Name   Title